PLEASURE
BEGETS
PLEASURE...

Pleasure lies not in any physical part. The center is in the mind. You are capable of knowing every pleasure by becoming aware of your own centers of sensuality. Through stimulation and self-control, you may progress to ever higher plateaus of joy. This is the whole of Tantra: the union of mind and body . . . learning to give the pleasure you seek, and to accept the pleasure given to you. Each step toward the knowledge of ecstasy moves you into new realms of your being.

Published by Jaico Publishing House
A-2 Jash Chambers, 7-A Sir Phirozshah Mehta Road
Fort, Mumbai - 400 001
jaicopub@jaicobooks.com
www.jaicobooks.com

Published in arrangement with
Dell Publishing Co., Inc.
1, Dag Hammarskjold Plaza
New York 10017

TANTRA: THE KEY TO SEXUAL POWER
ISBN 81-7224-073-2

First Jaico Impression: 1982
Eighteenth Jaico Impression: 2014

Printed by
Sanman & Co.
7/C/48, Sonawala Building
Tardeo, Mumbai - 400 007
E-mail: rajukothari1954@gmail.com

To the Tantrik Masters
Who Have Bestowed the
MARK OF THE MASTER
Upon My
Eternal
Essence
and
My
Physical
Presence

THE MEANING OF TANTRIC SEX

Tantric Sex is the ancient key to unbelievable sexual pleasure and psychic power, attained through a set of very special sexual rituals practiced by the "Hindu Cult of Ecstasy." It is a kind of "sexual magic" which brings pleasure, power, energy, and control.

Though the rituals have existed for thousands of years, they have been virtually unknown in the Western World.

They can enable you to reach indescribable new heights of sexual pleasure and at the same time tap your sexual energy for creative use in other areas of your life.

It took thousands of years for modern psychology to discover what the Tantric Masters have known all along: all animals, including man, are at their most intense state of conscious and subconscious concentration during sexual involvement. Through its rituals, Tantra teaches you to carry this intense concentration into all areas of your life.

The rituals will make it possible for you to enjoy sex more often, for longer periods of greater pleasure than you have ever known before. And the more frequently you have sex, the more quickly and powerfully your sexual energy will regenerate itself.

The word *Tantra* is the Sanskrit word meaning "the essence." It is derived from the verb *tantori*, "to weave"; hence the derivation *Tantra*, "the warp or essence of that which is woven."

of any differences between them. Male and Female are *one* in the eyes of Tantra. And Male and Female must strive to attain the transcendental enlightenment that will be theirs when they can once again experience the "wholeness" that makes them one. For, says the Tantra, "in that wholeness lies the supreme truth, total enlightenment."

On an earthly level, Male and Female join sexually through Tantric Rituals and thereby develop the power to move upward spiritually toward the cosmic whole, the one-ness that will bring them back to the total power of cosmic enlightenment which was theirs when they were but one Male-Female, joined beyond all time.

Tantra makes it possible for you to experience this transcendental sexual union through the ritualistic approach set forth in this book. This is not merely a sex manual or how-to-book. It will initiate you into a discipline which will put you in touch with the power of your sensuality and sexual energy. It will bring you heights of sexual pleasure. It will free you of self-consciousness and inhibitions. It will teach you to channel your immense sexual energy into all areas of your life.

Tantra knows no sexual frustration or inhibitions. Tantra integrates sexuality with the whole person. It enables the body, mind, and emotions to work together to give you power and control over your life and spiritual growth.

Tantra is free of the hypocrisy that pervades most Western and Hindu religious orders, which seek enlightenment and truth through asceticism (primarily self-denial in sex). Tantra believes the path to enlightenment is through increased sexual activity.

Tantra teaches that the ascetic road to wholeness and truth is self-defeating, a useless struggle.

In Tantra, all man's faculties—physical, mental, emotional—are stimulated as strongly as possible, then controlled, to bring ever-new pleasure.

A parable from one of the earliest Tantric texts, written in Sanskrit about two thousand years ago, tells of the hermit pilgrim who turned his back on all pleasure in search of *Parasamvit,* the "Supreme Truth." But no matter how far he traveled, nor how long he meditated and fasted, no matter how total his abstinence or how unbearable his self-inflicted pain, he never was able to reach that point of spiritual development where his concentrative powers were great enough to enable him to focus his total energy into the climb upward to the Supreme Truth.

Disillusioned, frustrated by years of unrewarded effort, he rested one late afternoon by the side of a stream. To that stream came a female Tantric Master, to bathe and anoint her body for the night of pleasure ahead. She talked to the pilgrim and, after hearing his story, she seduced him "carrying his senses through Tantric pleasures to the state of extremest arousal, wherein he found the center of power he sought, awaiting him in what he had so long denied himself."

Through the Awareness Rituals you will learn how to bring forth this sexual energy and retain it on a high plane, for your use at all times. Through the Control Rituals you will learn how to use your sensuality and sexual energy to bring forth sexual pleasure of an intensity you have never before dreamed possible. Through the Channeling Rituals you will learn how to direct this immense sexual energy to control your everyday activities, to control your mind, emotions, and body. You will be able to tap the source of creative energy and use that creativity to resolve problems or bring forth new ideas.

pervading sex, frequent and prolonged. And because of
the female's capacity for prolonged sexual activity and
repeated orgasm, she has—as at the creation—always
been the center of Tantric teaching. In earliest Tantric
texts, it was the woman who instructed in the rituals,
initiating all others into it. All organized Tantric groups
were led by women. Then, through the years, when
much of the Tantric literature was written by men,
screened through the minds of learned Brahmins and
others, the roles were reversed. Obviously, in the purest
sense of Tantric Sex, Female and Male are not only
equal, they are *one*. They may teach each other or
learn together.

There are many other aspects of Tantra, enough to
fill the several thousand books that have been written
on the subject: books encompassing not only the original Tantric texts but also the influences of Tantra on
yoga, Buddhism, and many other orders; books filled
with legends, history, philosophy, and doctrines that
have evolved from and revolved around the Tantra.

This book is concerned primarily with the simplest
and purest forms of Tantric Sex: that is, the basic
physical, mental, emotional, psychic, and sexual rituals.

The rituals have been taken from long research and
experience in Tantric studies. They are interpreted in
modern terms, with much of the language of Eastern
mysticism stripped away.

There are separate sections for Female and Male
rituals to be done alone. These may be the only portions of Tantra you wish to pursue. Within themselves,
these rituals teach all the basic Awareness, Control, and
Channeling necessary.

The book then proceeds to the section of Rituals for
Couples, "The Seven Nights of the Tantra." While written for heterosexual couples, the Rituals of the Seven

Nights of the Tantra are equally intended for, and adaptable for, use by homosexual couples.

The rituals themselves are to be enjoyed. Each is intended to bring pleasure, for the Tantra is always positive in its approach.

You will find as much pleasure in the pursuit of the goals of Tantric Sex as in attaining them. This ritualistic approach to sexual pleasure and fulfillment will bring to you an ever-increasing flow of sexual energy to fuel satisfaction of your every desire in life.

In the words of the Tantric Master:

"May I bring you sensual awareness, sexual ecstasy, and power over life."

Ashley Thirleby,
London

THE MANTRA

A *mantra* is a special sound, usually without meaning, which is used in Tantric rituals to trigger mental images (yantras), emotions, or controls. It is a vital part of the conditioning process of the rituals.

The classic mantric sound is *om*—the "sound of enlightenment." The earliest Tantric Masters were aware that even the most heavy and dense objects in our physical world are actually "vibrating substances," (the movement of atoms and molecules). Similarly, the structure of all life forms is based on a "vibrating rhythm."

The mantra puts the mind in tune with the vibrations, operating on their frequencies, to open the body's *chakras,* the natural orifices through which all psychic energy flows. The mantric sounds can condition the body, mind, and emotions to respond involuntarily to stimulate or control even the most basic emotions, thought patterns, or bodily functions.

The mantras are used in conjunction with the yantras (visual images). They are chanted or whispered or repeated silently to oneself during the Tantric rituals. They may be "written" on the visualization of imagery called the yantra. The "conditioning" thus uses both the senses of sight and sound.

Anyone who has studied behavioral psychology knows the story of Pavlov, who rang a bell when he fed his dogs, and after a while, whenever the bell was rung the dogs would salivate. This is conditioning at its most basic. Tantric conditioning is more complex, but it is nonetheless a conditioning process.

By consciously using the mantras together with physical stimuli and controls, you create a "trigger" that will cause a subconscious reaction which you would not otherwise be able to control. In modern psychological terms, the role of the mantra in Tantric ritual is to condition your sexual energy so you can control it, rather than have it control you.

Though Tantric mantras have no obvious meaning, they do follow a specified form, usually ending in a nasal humming, most often the "——omm" or "——ahm" sounds.

The Tantric masters teach that the sounds of the mantras set up energy fields, creating vibrations in patterns that can be controlled.

The rituals contained in this book use three mantras:

The mantra of Awareness

The mantra of Control

The mantra of Channeling

Each will be introduced at the beginning of the appropriate rituals.

They should be memorized and practiced only in conjunction with the rituals in which they serve a specific purpose.

THE YANTRA

Human beings would have a difficult time surviving without that fantastic faculty called *imagination*. Tantric Ritual relies heavily on the controlled use of the imagination called *yantras.*

In the ancient scripts of the Tantra, many of the yantras are symbolic icons that focus concentration on specific mental images to evoke stimulation or control of the senses.

But the images evoked, rather than the icons themselves, are of primary importance. For this reason, the icons are unnecessary in performing the rituals. Instead you will be taught, in the manner of the Tantric Masters, to project the images of the yantra directly onto the blackboard of your mind.

In Awareness, it is the imagery of the yantra that turns on the sexual drive. Using only the yantra imagery and the mantra sound of Awareness (stimulation), many Tantrics can bring themselves to the point of orgasm, then control the orgasm itself—thus maintaining an extremely high level of sexual energy—with no physical stimulation at all.

Control of stimulation—indeed, control of the actual orgasm—is attained through the sound of the Control Mantra, used in conjunction with the Control Yantra. Stimulation is turned off simply by concentrating on "writing" the words of the mantra on the black void of yantra imagination.

The Channeling yantra image, used with the Channeling mantra sound, will enable you to move the power of sexual energy into other areas of life: solving problems, aiding creativity, easing tensions and anxieties.

THE ONE-HOUR RULE

The rituals you will follow are totally sexually oriented. Neither sexual relations nor masturbation are ever discouraged in Tantra.

But the basic key to Tantric Sex is controlled pleasure. You must learn to exercise Control in order to reach the higher levels of pleasure the Tantra offers you.

Even the earliest Tantriks were aware of the difficulty of refraining from carrying each ritual to its logical, desirable conclusion: orgasm. Tantric texts tell of many initiates who gave in, repeatedly, to the desire for sexual satisfaction before they reached a point where they could follow the rituals precisely and move to higher plateaus of pleasure.

When you begin the rituals, you will find that they bring you quickly to a highly excited sexual state. As you proceed with each new ritual, the excitement will become more intense. And with that intensity, greater sexual energy is generated. It is that *energy* you will utilize to bring you previously unknown pleasure and power.

Because of the importance of controlling sexual energy, the One-Hour Rule evolved.

The Rule

For one hour *before* or *after* any Tantric ritual, you must *not* masturbate or have sexual relations.

Example: If you masturbate or have sex at 10:00 P.M. on a given evening, do not practice any ritual until after 11:00 P.M.

Conversely, if you complete a ritual at 11:00 P.M., you must neither masturbate nor have sexual relations until after 12:00 A.M.

The Rule is simple and explicit. To enjoy the full rewards of pleasure and power the Tantra brings, you must observe it.

THE TANTRA SAYS—

The Hands

Tantriks place special emphasis on the care of the hands, "the tactile instruments from which pleasure is drawn." The rituals often specify use of the thumb and index finger of both the right and left hands. Tantric texts direct the Tantrik to "trim short as possible the nails of the thumb and forefingers to avoid causing pain and unwanted abrasions."

The nails should be trimmed short enough to make the thumbs and index fingers "a smoothly rounded cylinder—a unit for the pleasure of touching." Indeed, many Tantriks recognize each other by observing the carefully manicured nails of the thumb and index fingers.

The Genitals

Tantric texts devote much space to the care and cleanliness of the genitals. The hygenic reasons for this are obvious, as are the esthetic ones.

But, say the Tantra texts, there is another reason: the use of a warm, wet cloth to cleanse the genitals is yet another effective method of developing awareness of one's sexuality. The logic of this will become more apparent as you proceed with the Awareness Rituals.

Many Tantriks make their cleanliness a ritual. The use of the bidet makes this easier. But even without such a convenience, a deliberately planned program of genital cleanliness is important.

The Lights

"Tantra abhors darkness."

Practice all Tantric Rituals in the light—never in a darkened room.

Darkness deprives you of the sense of sight and Tantric Sexual Rituals are designed to stimulate all the senses. You would not want to reduce the value of the Rituals by 20%, and that is what you would do if you chose to practice them in darkness.

Instructions for specific lighting are set forth in the preface to the Couples' Rituals, "The Seven Nights of the Tantra."

Food

The Tantra places no special emphasis on food, except that it suggests the enjoyment of those foods which are usually forbidden in high-caste Hindu society: meat, alcohol, fish, and grains.

Wine, cheese, and bread are recommended as the repast during the "Seven Nights of the Tantra," but they are not mandatory.

Tantra believes that you are free to enter into any activity you wish in life, and that you should do whatever you can to stimulate all of the senses to their highest degree. Such stimulation is recognized by the Tantra as being a highly individual matter.

Consent and Commitment

The Tantrik arrives at the epicenter of enlightenment only after a ritualistic climb.

Tantra forbids that any act ever be committed by a Tantrik which infringes upon the human rights of another. A Tantric Master will not ever attempt to *persuade* a non-Tantric to enter into Tantric Rituals.

Commitment, says the Tantra, must come from within.

No one is proselytized into Tantric thinking or activity.

You must arrive at the point of choice and enter into the rituals with the consent of your whole being, with total commitment.

The Meaning of "Love"

In most languages, and specifically in English, the word *love* is extremely difficult to define adequately.

But in the Tantric sense, the word is easily defined. Because Tantra is free of inhibition, there are no "hang-ups" to draw romantic and social connotations into the use of so simple a word.

Tantra, as you recall, means "essence."

Love, in the Tantric sense, means simply: "I recognize and accept your essence."

ABOUT THE RITUALS

All power, says the Tantra, derives from accumulated knowledge based on experience, starting with the simplest rituals and progressing to the most difficult, without losing the basic simplicities.

Some of the rituals, particularly the Awareness concepts, are deceptively simple. But they must not be by-passed. Awareness is a most important part of Tantric development.

Each part of each ritual must be practiced precisely as outlined in the following pages. It may be unclear in the beginning why certain ideas and instructions are included. And, indeed, their meaning may never become "logically" clear. But each instruction is an integral part of Tantric Ritual.

The exercises form a logical progression: *Awareness*

and *Sexual Pleasure; Sexual Control;* and the *Channeling of Sexual Power*.

Each Tantric student reaches the plateaus of accomplishment at a different speed, depending upon the intensity of practice. Some are content with the development of Awareness, increased sexual pleasure, and Control; others strive for the ultimate ability to channel their sexual drive, power, and concentration into their everyday living, decision-making, and creative processes. Each individual may evolve his own goals and his own level of attainment.

I encourage you to read this entire book before beginning the rituals. Except for obvious physical differences, the Male Alone and Female Alone Rituals contain much of the same information.

After reading the rituals that you will practice alone, "The Seven Nights of the Tantra," and the "Special Ritual" section through to the Conclusion, you will have sufficient understanding of the Rituals to decide how far into Tantra you wish to go.

You may wish to commit yourself only to the rituals practiced alone. Mastery of these will bring you a totally new Awareness of your own sensuality and sexuality. At the same time you will learn how to increase your sexual powers through Control, and how to Channel your sexual energy into other areas of your life.

Once you have mastered the Alone Rituals, you may proceed to the Couples' Rituals. This requires consent and commitment from both you and your partner, who should also have mastered the Alone Rituals.

It will take a week or more to master the Alone Rituals, depending on the time and effort you devote to them. Continue practicing the Alone Rituals even after proceeding to the Couples' Rituals; indeed you should practice the rituals as long as you live.

If you should lose Control at any point in the rituals and have an orgasm, do not be discouraged and give up. It happens at one time or another to all Tantric students. The object is to follow the rituals as precisely as possible—and enjoy them!

The Couples' Rituals are called "The Seven Nights of the Tantra." If at all possible, these rituals should be practiced on seven consecutive nights. If this is not possible, they should be done in as short a time as is possible—every other night for two weeks, for example. But you must practice them in the order written.

You will find that your sexual energy will increase greatly with practice of the Awareness Rituals. Your control of sexual energy will grow with each repetition of the Control Ritual. And your entire being will grow in self-confidence, calmness, and total power as you repeat the Channeling Rituals.

THE
FEMALE
ALONE
RITUALS

THE MANTRA OF AWARENESS

The sound: *Ommm. Ahdi. Ommm.*

Learn and use only in conjunction with these Rituals. It may be said barely audibly, or repeated silently to oneself, or chanted aloud. The described yantra imagery should always accompany the mantra.

AWAKENING

In the beginning, when the Goddess of Time, Kali, took unto herself the human female form, it was new to her. No longer was she solely the creative force, depleting energy to create anew. She now endowed herself with sensuality and sexuality and her pleasure was in the new discovery of herself.

We all know our own bodies, but somehow living with them every day we tend to neglect their pervasive sensuality. The Tantra begins by teaching us to know our bodies anew, in a Tantric way; a more intimate, uninhibited sensual way.

Stand nude in front of a large mirror and concentrate on your reflection. First focus on your lips and bring the index fingers of both hands up to touch the lips lightly, sliding the fingers along the edges. Feel your lips quiver and respond to the touch as if another's fingers were creating the sensation.

Now bring your left hand to the right breast. Concentrate on the form of the breast and nipple, and apply enough pressure to create a pleasing sensation—a very light stroking. Become aware of the sensitivity of the breast. Feel the nipple harden as you continue stroking and repeat two Awareness Mantras in an audible whisper.

Now drop the left hand to your side, softly stimulate your left breast with your right hand, again repeating two Awareness Mantras. The saying of the mantras intensifies the gentle pleasure of touching and stroking the breast and nipple. Trace the nipple itself with your fingertips. Become aware of the subtle differences of each part of the breast.

Now fold the hands and let them rest, relaxed against the abdomen just below the navel. Say an Awareness Mantra and, parting the hands, slide the fingers and palms downward across the abdomen, through the pubic hair, to the vagina, and apply just enough pressure to feel the warm awareness of the caress.

As the hands press gently upon the vaginal lips, repeat the Awareness Mantra twice. Then relax the hands and let them hang loosely by the sides.

This is the first phase of the ritual.

Now, close your eyes tight. Concentrate on your body until a clear image (yantra) of your reflection in the mirror is firmly fixed in your mind. If you have a little trouble establishing the image, open your eyes and take a long look at your body. Touch your lips, breasts, and vagina again. Repeating the touch will help fix the image in your mind.

With eyes closed, repeat the ritual. Again bring the

fingertips to the lips and concentrate on the sensation, while mentally picturing your lips being touched gently by hands that are not yours. Repeat the Awareness Mantra quietly as your fingers trace your lips.

Then move the hands to the breasts, as before, but with the eyes closed and the imagery (yantra) of hands belonging to another, stroking the breast, intensifying the pleasure.

Maintain the imagery of the hands of another person as they move downward and press against the vagina.

As you carry out each step of the ritual, hold in your mind the yantra of another's hands and repeat two Awareness Mantras.

Now repeat the ritual yet another time with the eyes closed, but this time, in your yantra imagine that the two hands are yours, but the lips, breast, and vagina you touch belong to another. Try to feel, with your fingertips, the outline of the lips of another, the breasts and nipples of another, the soft pubic hair through which the fingers and palms move, the ridged lips of the vagina—all as if exploring, gently, the parts of another's body.

As you do this, repeat the Awareness Mantras at each point in the ritual.

This deceptively simple ritual is both pleasurable and relaxing. Practice it first thing in the morning. It will make your body feel sensually alive and give you positive energy for the day ahead. And when you repeat it in the evening, it will gently relax you, and erase the tension of the day.

It should be done twice daily.

YANTRIC AWARENESS

And it is told that the Initiate asked of the Tantric Master, "Where lies the center of my pleasure? I feel it in all parts of my being. Yet as in the universe, it must have a center. Is this not true?"

And the Tantric Master disrobed herself and said to the Initiate: "Look upon my body as you would look upon your own. Know that the body is as one with the universe and the center of all its pleasure lies not in any physical part. The center is in the mind. The mind perceives the body's sensations. Our pleasure is what our mind perceives as pleasurable."

In the course of your normal activities during the day, pause at least once (twice or three times, if possible) and, eyes closed tightly, repeat your Awareness Mantra to yourself. Try to evoke the image of yourself standing before the mirror. Without actually touching yourself, use all your concentrative efforts to bring forth the images and the sensations you experienced as you touched your body, as you imagined another's hands touching you, and as you imagined touching another's body.

As you practice this daily, the image-creating yantra will become progressively easier. You will soon be able to call forth both the yantra imagery and the sensations by merely closing your eyes tightly and repeating the Awareness Mantra to yourself.

THE YANTRIC BODY

Kali gave to Woman total sexuality, the ability to know repeated pleasure infinitely. In so doing, Kali bestowed on the Female the capacity to control all parts of her body for her own pleasure and the pleasure of her mate.

"Female pleasure is the seat of all pleasure," says the Tantric Master. "As the Female develops her body's ability to derive pleasure, so shall she bring forth the ability to give pleasure."

This is a ritual of yantra imagery, but with physical muscular coordination added. It can be practiced anywhere, either fully clothed or in the nude.

First the imagery: try to picture the interior of your vagina as a passageway inside walls of muscles. While seated, standing, or lying down—and without touching any part of your body—close your eyes and, while repeating the Awareness Mantra, concentrate on this vaginal passageway-yantra.

Once the yantra is fixed, tightly contract the muscles of your vagina. This is approximately the same sensation you have when you control your bladder and bowel movements. Do not be concerned that the anal, thigh, and stomach muscles are also tightening. Picture only the tightening of the vaginal muscles. Repeat the Awareness Mantra and, each time you tighten the muscles, envision each muscle contracting. Once the muscles are tight, hold them tight while saying the mantra, then relax.

Repeat the tightening-relaxing process three times. This ritual may be repeated as often as desired and can be done virtually anywhere, once the imagery is mastered.

The ritual itself is sensually stimulating, and you will gradually become aware of the intricate construction of the vagina. Slowly the vaginal muscles will become conditioned and you will be able to sense the tightening of each set of muscles. The yantra imagery can be refined to picture the individual vaginal muscles, as you become aware of them.

FOCUSING

The Tantra worships no deities as such. Kali and Mahakala are called its "deities," but the Tantra makes definite observations regarding them:

"Kali, the Goddess of Time, exists now not as a personification to be worshiped. We build to her no idols. No temples. Yet she is at the center of all pleasure; she is at the center of all yantras; she is the center of all creative energy. But she is to be perceived within all females, not existing apart from them."

Based on this Tantric teaching, the Tantric Masters are commanded to "pass on to the initiate all learning in the form of pleasure, as did Kali to Mahakala, for the climb upward to Supreme Truth and Enlightenment is a climb of increased pleasure with each new plateau reached."

* * *

This ritual should be done on a bed, alone, preferably at night. Though it is extremely stimulating sexually, it should not be used as a prelude to masturbation or sexual relations. Here we apply the Tantric One-Hour Rule for the first time.

On a bed, completely nude, lie on your back and raise your knees to a comfortable position, feet together. Slowly allow the knees to separate and the soles of the feet to press against each other. The soles and heels of the right foot and left foot should remain in contact throughout the ritual.

In this position, fold your hands lightly across your abdomen at your navel.

Close your eyes tightly and, using the Awareness Mantra, focus totally on the yantra image of *yourself* lying in this position on the bed, as if your nude body belonged to someone else.

Raise your hands slowly, eyes still closed, and bring the index finger of each hand to your mouth. Envisioning an image of what you are doing, say the mantra twice while you softly slide the index fingers from side to side on your lips. Return your hands to the folded position on your abdomen.

Next bring the index finger and thumb of each hand up to the bottom of the left and right breast (left hand under left breast, right hand under right). Again, holding the yantra image of your actions, slowly slide the tips of the thumbs and index fingers upward on the breast to the nipples.

Repeat the Awareness Mantra twice slowly as you gently stimulate your nipple, "rolling it between your thumb and forefinger," then return your hands to your abdomen.

Pause briefly to reinforce the yantra in your mind,

then trace a path, with forefingers and thumbs, down through the pubic hair, and rest your hands between your legs, palms straight up and down on either side of the vaginal lips. Begin repeating the mantra as the palms turn slightly inward. Slowly move the thumbs toward the labia and, using only your thumbs, spread open the labia as far as is comfortable. The index fingers cross the thumbs and the tip of each index finger rests on the sides of the clitoris; the tip of each finger presses gently to stimulate the clitoris.

As you repeat the mantra, concentrate the imagery on the area you are touching. Do not massage the clitoris, only hold the labia open with your thumbs and press against the clitoris with your index fingers.

After repeating the mantra twice, return your hands to your abdomen.

In the same manner as in the Awakening Ritual, the visual image of the Mitual should once again be reinforced in the mind. Imagine someone else's hands caressing your body, then imagine that you are touching another's body, picturing your hands moving to the lips, then the breasts, then the vagina. Attempt to re-create in your mind the same yantra image you held while actually touching your body. Over a period of time, you will be able to "sense" the hands touching the lips, breasts, and vagina, without any actual physical contact.

This ritual has two distinct parts: first, the actual touching, imagery, and mantra; second, the imagery of touching, the creation of sensation by using only the yantra imagery and the mantra.

INTENSIFYING FOCUS

The initiate approached the Tantric Master and asked of her:

"Why must I seek pleasure in solitude? Is not the greater pleasure to be found in the arms of another? Is not the exchange of pleasure preferable to that found in solitude?"

And the Tantric Master replied:

"All pleasure is perceived within your being. You are capable of knowing all pleasure there is by becoming aware of your own centers of sensuality. Through stimulation, and self-control, you may reach all the plateaus of pleasure you may conceive in the image of your yantra.

"Once you know the centers of your pleasure, you will be better able to share pleasure with another. This is the whole of the Tantra: that you must perceive what you are through knowing yourself and your pleasures; for only then can you give the pleasure you seek and accept the pleasure given to you."

This ritual is an extension of the Focusing Ritual, which should be practiced for several days and "mastered" before adding these refinements.

Practice the Focusing Ritual and after you press against the sides of the clitoris, relax your index fingers and allow them to fall away from the clitoris. Then relax your thumbs and allow the labia to close. Keep your hands relaxed and resting on the vagina. Say the mantra twice, then, envisioning imagery of your action, slide the two index fingers downward, until they touch the perineum, that small space between the very bottom of the vaginal cleft and the anus. With the tips of the index fingers press against the perineum, while saying the mantra twice. Then return your hands to relax on your vagina. Then repeat the clitoral portion of the ritual, with thumbs opening the labia and index fingers pressing on the clitoris, while you repeat two mantras.

Now your hands should again rest on the vagina while you reinforce the yantra imagery and repeat the mantra twice.

Then again slide the index fingers downward, past the base of the vaginal opening, across the perineum, and touch the rectum. Pressing on the rectal muscle, repeat two mantras, then bring your hands back to rest relaxed atop your vagina.

Now repeat the clitoral pressure exercise once more, with the thumbs opening the labia and the index fingers pressing on the clitoris while you repeat two mantras.

Then return the hands to their position on the abdomen.

Now the total imagery aspect of the ritual should begin with imagery of fingers on lips, then breasts, then vagina-clitoris, then relaxed, then the perineum, then the clitoris again, then the rectum, then again the clitoris. Picture, in your mind, the hands of another touching you, then focus on the sensation of your own hands, touching the body of another.

Each step of the longer ritual should be taken deliberately and slowly.

The object is, of course, Awareness—not only Awareness of the sensitive parts of the body touched and held in imagery, but also an Awareness of the direct erotic links in your body.

This ritual is highly arousing, but it should go without saying that the One-Hour Rule must be observed. You are now beginning to learn to control your sexual energy.

PHYSICAL FOCUS

The body is the way of all pleasure, but the total, subtle body exists in the yantra. It cannot exist apart from the imagery of the mind.

All functions of the body are a part of Tantric teachings. This is the concept of this ritual, a simple procedure associated with the "Tantra Says" notations earlier in the book.

Tantric literature recognizes the dual purpose of the genito-urinary system, but rather than separating the functions, it uses the process of urination and the genital muscles used while urinating as a logical part of the Awareness Ritual.

After urinating, contract the vagina muscles one time, while saying one Awareness Mantra. Then, when possible, use a warm, damp cloth to cleanse the vaginal area. Place the index finger of your right hand on the tip of the clitoris and exert pressure while saying one mantra of Awareness.

It may not always be possible to use a warm cloth to cleanse the vagina, but the index-pressure on the clitoris should be done anyway. It is a sensual act that will raise your Awareness level, and at the same time will remove any inhibitions you may have about accepting your normal bodily functions and their relation to your sexuality.

CONTROL OF PLEASURE AND POWER

The Tantric Master spoke to her Initiates in these words:

"You have reached the plateau of understanding the pleasures your body affords you through the senses. And you have intermixed and focused these pleasures through the yantra and mantra. But your pleasure is only now beginning. To reach new heights of stimulation, you must first learn to control the senses of pleasure. Therein lie sexual feelings and energy and power beyond all you have ever dreamed before."

This is the single *most important* ritual in Tantra. It is the key to all that lies ahead.

The Control Mantra:

The sound: *Pahhh. Dahhh. O-mahmmm.*

It should be memorized by repeating it, when specified in the ritual.

The Control Ritual:

Lie on the bed, with the knees spread and the soles of the feet pressing against each other, and go through your regular Focusing Ritual, continuing into the Intensifying Focus Ritual.

At the end of these rituals, after saying the Awareness Mantra, return your hands to the vagina as before. Use the thumbs to open the labia and the index fingers to press on the clitoris.

Say the Awareness Mantra as you gently massage the clitoris with your right index finger while you trace the vagina and urethral opening with the index finger of the left hand.

Keep the Awareness Mantra in mind, and envision yourself masturbating as you begin to masturbate. Do whatever feels best to you. But be sure to maintain the basic position and the yantra imagery of yourself masturbating yourself, or of being masturbated by another. Naturally other sexual imagery will arise. Fantasies will play in your mind. This is desirable, so long as the Awareness Mantra and Yantra are also present and an important part of your pleasure.

As soon as you feel on the verge of orgasm, you should immediately begin saying the Control Mantra. Remove your hands from your vagina, and fold them across your abdomen. You will be highly aroused but you must refrain from further masturbation, and continue to repeat (loudly if it helps) the Control Mantra.

As soon as you start saying the Control Mantra, immediately change your yantra imagery. Concentrate and conjure in your mind a giant void of blackness on which the words of the Control Mantra—*pahhh, dahhh, o-mahmmm*—are written. Try to banish all other thought and images from your mind. This yantric concentration is as important as removing your hands and ceasing masturbating. This, with the sound of the mantra itself, is your key to Control.

As you fight for this Control, you will find you are still sexually stimulated but your arousal is under your Control.

Lie on the bed until you feel you have attained the complete Control created by your yantra and mantra. Then you should rise and do whatever you wish: have a glass of wine, or watch television, or read, or go out, or prepare to go to sleep. But you must not masturbate or engage in sexual relations for at least one hour.

While going about your normal routine after this ritual, your sexual drive will be very strong. Whenever you feel a need to go back and masturbate, or have sexual relations in any form, repeat the Control Mantra and use the Control Yantra imagery to maintain your control.

If after one hour has passed, you engage in any form of sex, you will find that, having completed the Control Ritual, your sexual energy is increased. You will reach a higher level of sexual stimulation and greater, more intense satisfaction. Enjoy the increase in your sexual pleasure; right now you don't need to be concerned with Tantric Control.

The first time you try this exercise will be the most difficult. Each succeeding time, you will find Control comes a little more easily. After a while, you will be able to draw closer and closer to the actual point of orgasm and still be able to pull back with Tantric Control. The stronger your Control becomes, the better. It is not unusual, once complete Control is established, to continue masturbating while the mantra and yantra imagery of control are used. You will then be able to sustain yourself on the verge of orgasm indefinitely, while controlling it completely. This of course comes with time and regular practice of the Awareness and Control Rituals.

Initiates often ask whether this Control Ritual should be performed nightly, as an extension of the Focusing and Intensifying Focus Rituals. The answer is *yes*. Just as the Awareness Rituals are part of establishing a daily pattern, so this all-important Control Ritual must be part of the conditioning process. To be able to heighten Awareness, pleasure, and Control, the patterns must be established and practiced regularly.

Another question is often asked about the Control Exercise and menstruation. Tantra texts consider menstruation merely another normal function of a healthy body. The Awareness and Control Rituals should be practiced nightly, even during menstruation. Using a tampon makes this easier, but even without it, the Tantric texts insist that the rituals be carried out daily.

Now you are beginning to see that these rituals proceed in a logical sequence designed to gradually bring heightened sexual pleasure, while enabling you to have Control over it.

This is the most important single ritual of the Tantra. It may appear the most difficult to master, but if you follow the instructions carefully and practice with determination, mindful of the objectives to be gained, you will soon master it.

Now we move on to a logical extension of this Control Ritual: the Channeling of Sexual Power.

CHANNELING POWER AND ENERGY

The Tantra tells this story of the "first humans" brought
forth by Kali and Mahakala:

*All were Tantric Masters at the beginning. They
multiplied and initiated all into the knowledge and
pleasures of Tantra. But succeeding generations became
so engrossed in pleasure, they lost the knowledge of using their sexual energy for creative purposes in their
lives.*

*Each Tantrik was a master of pleasure and Control,
to heighten pleasure. But the regenerated power and
energy filled them with anxiety, for they had no purpose for it beyond that of pleasure.*

*The Tantra tells the story of that female Tantric Mas-
ter who heightened her sensitivity and pleasure each
day, but could not find the key for Channeling this great
energy to other parts of her being. The search itself
caused her great frustration. She became nervous and
unhappy—even amid the sensual pleasures she experienced.*

*Then, one night, as she held her lover in her arms
and drew pleasure from him, her mind, emotions, and
body reeled with a vision; she was enveloped by the
duality of Kali and Mahakala. They fired her body to
such heights of ecstasy that she entered a trance-like
state, on the verge of an orgasm that would not occur
because Kali repeatedly wrote the yantra of Control on
her mind while Mahakala entered her from below and
whispered the mantra of Control into her ear.*

Suspended between the taut heights of pleasure and Control, she suddenly heard a new mantra from Mahakala, while Kali pictured on the blackness of her mind all of the practical everyday things which the woman desired in life.

Suddenly Kali and Mahakala were gone, but they had bestowed on this Tantric Master the great secret of Tantra: Controlled Channeling.

She had relearned the secret which had become lost. And she taught the secret to her lover, and to all those who would learn. And she worshiped Kali and Mahakala, and founded anew the great cult of ecstasy known as Tantra.

The Channeling Mantra

The sound: *Ahh. Nahh. Yahh. Tawnnn.*

The Channeling Ritual

You have established the nightly ritual of Awareness, progressed through the Focusing and Intensifying Focus Rituals, and carried these through to the Control Ritual. You have reached the point where you are on the verge of orgasm. You remove your hands and cease masturbation. You are bringing about Control through the use of the Control Mantra and Yantra.

Your hands are folded across your abdomen and you are still in the position on the bed, nude, knees apart, soles of feet pressed together.

Through the Control Mantra and Yantra, you have reached a point where you feel you have attained control; you have stopped the impending orgasm and, though you would *like* to continue masturbating or have sex relations, you will not because you are in control and will not violate the One-Hour Rule.

When you reach this point, you may begin the rewarding Tantric process of Channeling.

This is the procedure:

When you have attained Control, retain your position and cease the Control Mantra and Yantra. You may resume them, of course, if the urgent desire for sexual satisfaction overtakes you.

Now, fix in your mind the image of some everyday situation or problem that has been bothering you. You may have decided prior to beginning, precisely what problem or situation you will choose for Channeling.

Suppose you have a serious problem to solve, or a decision to make; or suppose you have been irritable and nervous. Start thinking about the problem as soon as you attain Control. Isolate it. Start saying the Channeling Mantra over and over, while "writing" the words identifying the problem, on the black void of imagery.

This will begin a conditioning process that channels your highly stimulated sexual concentration into the resolution of the problem.

The process is deceptively simple:

You have attained Control.

You are ready to Channel your energy.

You retain your position on the bed and start saying the Channeling Mantra over and over, alternating it with an isolated statement of the problem, as follows:

"Ahh. Nahhh. Yahh. Tawnnn. I will remain more calm and patient. Be at peace within myself and with others. *Ahh. Nahh. Yahh. Tawnnn."*

Or:

"Ahh. Nahh. Yahh. Tawnnn. The right idea for solving the problem about ———— will come to me. I am creative. The answer will come. *Ahh. Nahh. Yahh. Tawnnn."*

Repeat the process six times, presenting the same problem or desire each of the six times. Keep the wording simple, and repeat it. Your mind already *knows* the *details* of the problem, so all you want is a few words to direct concentration to it. To intensify that concentration, "write" the words you are saying to yourself (mantra included) on the black void of imagery.

Once you have repeated the Channeling six times, cease the Channeling Mantra and stop thinking about the problem or the process.

Now recite the Control mantra two times.

Then repeat twice the Awareness mantra. Remove your hands from your stomach and get up from the bed.

Now, observing the One-Hour Rule, go about your regular routine. Many Tantriks perform the Awareness, Control, and Channeling Rituals about one to two hours before they go to bed to sleep. They arise after the exercise, have a glass of wine, a hot bath, then, after the hour has passed, go to bed, prepared for sex or just for sleep.

You will still be in a sexually stimulated state. Use the Control Mantra, along with the Control Imagery, to maintain Control during the One Hour, or longer, if you wish.

Do not expect the answer or solution to the problem you presented during Channeling to suddenly pop into your mind. Try not to dwell on it. Your ally, your sexual concentrative power, is now subconsciously at work for you.

At some unexpected moment, the answer will surface. Or you will realize that the desired results are being achieved.

And with each passing night of practicing the Awareness, Control, and Channeling Rituals, all of your powers will increase.

THE
MALE
ALONE
RITUALS

THE MANTRA OF AWARENESS

The Sound: *Ommm. Ahdi. Ommm.*

Learn this mantra for use only with the Awareness Rituals. It may be said barely audibly, or silently to oneself. The described yantra imagery should always accompany the mantra.

AWAKENING

Mahakala looked upon the reflection of the body Kali had given to him. And he touched his body, to know the sensations of pleasure to be derived from it. And Kali directed his touch, and taught him all there was to know.

You know what your body looks like, but living with it everyday you may not appreciate it as the fine sensual organism it can be. The Tantra begins by teaching you to know your body "the Tantric way," a more uninhibited way.

Stand nude in front of a large mirror. Focus on your lips and bring the index and middle fingers of your right hand to your lips. Feel your lips; respond as if another person were creating the sensation, and repeat the Awareness Mantra once.

Now bring your left hand to the nipple of the right

breast. Concentrate on the form of the nipple. Become aware of its sensitivity. Feel the nipple harden. After you repeat two Awareness Mantras, move the hand away.

Let your left hand drop to your side. Now gently stimulate your left breast with your right hand, while repeating two Awareness Mantras. Saying the mantras intensifies the pleasure of stroking the nipple.

Now fold your hands and let them relax against the abdomen just below the naval. Say the mantra. Parting your hands, slide them downward, through the pubic hair.

With the index finger and thumb, encircle your penis at its base and tighten your fingers around it while you repeat one Awareness Mantra. Then move your hand away from your penis, without touching any other part of it.

This is phase one of the ritual.

Now, close your eyes very tightly. Concentrate on a detailed Yantra image of yourself in the nude—an image of your reflection in the mirror. If you have trouble establishing the image, open your eyes and look again at the reflection of your body. Touch your lips, nipples, and penis again. Repeating the touch will help fix the image in your mind.

With eyes closed, repeat the ritual. Touch your fingers to your lips while mentally picturing that the hands touching your lips belong to someone else. Repeat the mantra as you do this. Then move your fingers to your left breast, applying pressure on the nipple as before, maintaining the image of someone else's fingers touching the nipple, intensifying the pleasure as you say the mantra.

Do this with the right nipple, then slide the hands downward, with the yantra of someone else's fingers encircling the base of your penis, applying pressure. The sensation will be even stronger than you experienced with your eyes open.

Now repeat the ritual yet another time with your eyes closed, but this time imagine that the hand is yours but it is touching the lips, nipples, and penis of someone else. Let your fingertips sense the soft outline of another's lips; your fingers sense the hardening of the nipples of another person's breast; your hands slide through soft pubic hair; your fingers encircle the base of a penis belonging to another person—all exploring the body of someone else.

This deceptively simple ritual is both relaxing and stimulating. Practice it in the morning. It will make you feel sensually alive and well all day.

When repeated in the evening, it will put your body in a state of restful relaxation.

It should be done twice daily.

YANTRIC AWARENESS

The story is told of the Initiate who asked of the Tantric Master; "What is the center of my pleasure? As all things move in harmony with the universe, each must have its center. Yet I feel pleasure throughout my being."

And the Tantric Master replied:

"Pleasure lies only in that which the mind perceives as pleasurable. The center of your being and your pleasure is within your mind."

*   *   *

In the course of your normal activities during the day, pause at least once (twice or three times, if possible) and, eyes closed tight, try to evoke the image of yourself standing before the mirror. Without actually touching yourself, use all your concentrative efforts to bring forth the image, and the sensations of pleasure you experienced as you touched each part of your body, and as you imagined your hands touching someone else's body.

As you practice this daily, the image-creating yantra will come to you more easily. You will soon be able to call forth both the yantra imagery and the sensations by merely closing your eyes tightly and repeating the Awareness Mantra to yourself.

THE YANTRIC BODY

As Kali taught the pleasures and power of Tantra to Mahakala, she directed that he should be aware of every facet of his own being, so that he might derive all pleasure from it. He learned to create for himself repeated erections of his penis, and revel in the sensations it afforded him. For Kali knew that, as the Male derived pleasure, so he would desire more pleasure, and would learn to give pleasure to create his own satisfaction.

This is a ritual of yantra imagery, but with physical, muscular coordination added.

First the imagery: try to picture your penis as a shaft or tube with muscles supporting it, muscles running from deep within you and enveloping the organ. Also picture hollow tubes crisscrossed among the muscles—tubes waiting to fill and create an erection.

While seated or lying down—without touching your body—close your eyes, and while repeating the Awareness Mantra, concentrate on this image of your penis.

Once the yantra is fixed, contract tightly all the muscles running through the penis. This is approximately the same sensation as tightly "squeezing" for bladder and bowel control.

Do not be concerned that the anal, thigh, and stomach muscles are also tightening. Picture only the tightening of the penile muscles, and the filling of the tubes. Once the muscles are tight, say the Awareness Mantra once, then relax.

Repeat the tightening-relaxing process three times. This ritual may be repeated as often as desired and can be done virtually anywhere, once the yantra imagery is mastered.

Gradually the muscles of the penis will become conditioned and you will be able to sense the tightening of each set of muscles involved. You will become more aware of the intricate construction of the penis. The ritual itself is sensually stimulating and will prove to be an aid in controlling erection.

FOCUSING

The Tantric Master spoke to each of his disciples, saying:

"The rituals of solitude bring forth awareness of be-

*ing. From awareness in solitude, the pleasures of your
body shall be learned. For you must first know the
sensuality that brings forth pleasure before you can
direct another to bring forth pleasure for you. And you
must know your own pleasure before you possess the
power to give pleasure to another."*

This ritual should be done on a bed, alone, preferably at night. Though it is extremely stimulating sexually, it should not be used as a prelude to masturbation
or sexual relations. Here we apply the Tantric One-
Hour Rule for the first time.

On a bed, completely nude, on your back, raise the
knees to a comfortable position, feet together. Slowly
allow the knees to separate and the soles of the feet to
press against each other. The soles and heels of the
right foot and left foot should remain in contact
throughout the ritual.

In this position, fold your hands across your abdomen at your navel. Close your eyes tight and, using
the Awareness Mantra, focus your mind totally on an
image of yourself lying in this position on the bed, as if
your nude body belonged to someone else.

Raise your hands slowly, eyes still closed, and bring
the index finger of each hand to your mouth. Mentally
holding the image of what you are doing, say the mantra twice while you softly slide the index fingers side to
side on your lips. Return your hands to the folded position on your abdomen.

Next bring the index finger and thumb of each hand
up to the nipple of each breast (left hand to left nipple,
right hand to right nipple). Again, holding the yantra
image of your actions, take each nipple between the
thumb and forefinger and "roll" it slightly, to create

a stimulating, pleasant feeling, as you recite two mantras. Then the hands return to the abdomen.

Pause briefly to reinforce the yantra in your mind, then move your hands slowly, tracing a path with forefingers and thumbs, down through the pubic hair, and rest your hands, palms straight up and down between your legs, on either side of your penis. Begin repeating the Mantra as your palms turn inward. The thumbs rest above the base of your penis. The index fingers wrap round the bottom of the base of your penis. Now tighten your fingers around your penis as you say the mantra three times, maintaining the yantra imagery of action.

Do not massage the penis or genital area; use only the squeezing action of fingers and thumbs, then return the hands to the abdomen.

In the same manner as in the Awakening Ritual, the visual image of the ritual should once again be reinforced in the mind; imagine someone else's hands caressing your body, then imagine you are touching another's body. Picture the hands moving to the lips, to the nipples, then to the penis. Attempt to re-create in your mind the same yantra image you held while actually touching your body. Over a period of time, you will develop the ability to "sense" the hands touching your lips, nipples, and penis, without any actual physical contact.

This ritual has two distinct parts: first, the actual touching, yantra imagery, and mantra; second, the yantra imagery of touching, creating the sensation by imagery alone, using the mantra as an aid.

After a while, using only the imagery and the mantra, you will be able to create these stimulating sensations at any time, any place.

INTENSIFYING FOCUS

*The Initiate asked of the Tantric Master: "How shall
I know that I have become a master of pleasure? Surely
I cannot know this, too, only alone."*

*And the Tantric Master replied: "Each step moves
you into new realms of your being—realms you could
not know had you not taken the smaller previous step.
In such a manner, pleasure begets pleasures through
the rituals of knowing yourself."*

This ritual is an extension of the Focusing Ritual
which should be practiced for several days and "mastered" before adding these refinements.

Practice the Focusing Ritual and after you squeeze
the base of the penis, relax the thumbs and index fingers
from their grip on your penis. Say the mantra again
and slide the index fingers downward, following the
outline of the penis base until you reach the deepest
perceptible "bottom end" on the penis roots, within the
scrotum. Exert just enough pressure to create a pleasing sensation.

Say the mantra once, then relax the index fingers and
rest for a moment. Reinforce the yantra image.

Now let slide the index fingers down around the
testicles to rest on the perineum, that area between the
base of the penis-scrotum and the anus. Press inward
on the perineum while saying the mantra twice.

Now slide the index fingers around the scrotum,
across the perineum, until they press on the rectal

muscles and create a pleasant sensation. This pressure should be maintained through two mantras.

Then once again wrap thumbs and index fingers around the penis base and squeeze.

Then return your hands to their position on your abdomen.

Now the total yantra imagery aspect of this ritual should begin. Without actually touching the body, create the *imagery* of fingers on lips, then nipples, abdomen; around the penis, downward into the scrotum; to the perineum; to the rectal muscles; around the penis's base; then back to the folded position on the abdomen.

Each step of this longer ritual should be taken deliberately and slowly.

The object is of course, Awareness—not only Awareness of the sensitive parts of the body touched, but also an awareness of the direct erotic links of your body.

This is a very stimulating ritual, but it must be followed by the One-Hour Rule. The ritual, and the period of an hour afterward, are the beginning of your learning to control your sexual energy.

PHYSICAL FOCUS

All that exists, exists within the mind. The physical body is but an extension of the subtle body which exists within the imagery of the yantra.

The body and all its functions are related to the yantra and to pleasure.

*   *   *

This simple ritual is associated with the "Tantra Says" notations earlier in the book.

Tantric literature recognizes the dual purpose of the genito-urinary system, but rather than separating the functions, it uses the process of urination, and the genital muscles used while urinating, as a logical part of the Awareness Ritual.

After urinating, consciously tighten all the muscles surrounding the penis, twice or three times, while saying one Awareness Mantra.

As you normally "shake" your penis to remove drops of urine, slide your right index finger and thumb to the base of the penis and, squeezing the penis, slide them in a single slow movement from the base of the penis to the tip. This will remove any excess urine remaining in the urethra, and at the same time reinforce the Awareness Rituals and leave a stimulating sexual feeling. It will also help remove any inhibitions you may have about accepting your normal bodily functions and their relation to your sexuality.

CONTROL OF PLEASURE AND POWER

The Tantric Master spoke to his Initiates in these words:
"You have reached the plateau of understanding the pleasures your body affords you through the senses. And you have intermixed and focused these pleasures through the yantra and mantra. But your pleasure is only now beginning. To reach new heights of stimulation, you must first learn to control the senses of plea-

sure. Therein lie sexual feelings and energy and power beyond all you have ever dreamed before."

This is the single *most important* ritual in Tantra. It is the key to all that lies ahead.

The Control Mantra

The sound: *Pahhh. Dahhh. O-mahhh.*

It should be committed to memory by chanting it softly or loudly or to oneself, as specified in the exercises.

The Control Ritual

Lying on the bed, with the knees spread and the bottoms of the feet pressing against each other, go through the regular Focusing Ritual, continuing into the Intensifying Focus Ritual.

At the end of these rituals, after saying the Awareness Mantra the final time, return your hands again to your penis, gripping it with the index fingers and thumbs, as before.

Say the Awareness Mantra. Continue gripping the penis and slide the fingers away from the base of the penis, up the shaft to the tip. Relax the squeezing pressure and slide the fingers back downward to the base of the penis. Then squeeze and slide back to the tip. Using these movements, concentrate on the yantra imagery of your actions, to stimulate your penis to an erection and begin to masturbate. The exact movements of the fingers and thumbs now become a matter of personal preference. But the position on the bed, soles of

feet pressed together, must be maintained. If you prefer, use one hand (or finger and thumb) to stimulate
the penis, while the other finger and thumb touch and
press the scrotum, perineum, and anal opening. Naturally, other sexual imagery will arise. This is fine as
long as you also keep the Awareness Mantra and the
Yantra as part of your pleasure.

As soon as you feel the urge of orgasm, you should
immediately begin saying the Control Mantra, and remove your hands from your penis and fold them across
your abdomen. You will be highly aroused, but you
must refrain from further masturbation and continue
to repeat (loudly, if it helps) the Control Mantra. If
at first you feel that orgasm might occur even after you
remove your hands, you should use the thumb and index finger of the right hand to "pinch" tightly the tip of
the penis. This will numb the penile nerve endings and
prevent ejaculation. But this must be done quickly,
and then the fingers removed and the hands returned to
the abdomen.

As soon as you start saying the Control Mantra, immediately change your yantra imagery. Concentrate,
and conjure up in your mind a giant void of blackness
on which the words of the Control Mantra—*pahhh,
dahhh, o-mahhh*—are written. This yantric concentration of blackness is as important as removing your
hands and ceasing masturbation. This, with the sound
of the mantra itself, is, your *key to Control.*

As you fight for this control, you will find you are
still sexually excited but your stimulation is under your
Control.

Continue to lie on the bed until you feel you have
attained complete Control created by your mantra and
yantra. Then you should rise and do whatever you

wish: have a glass of wine, or watch television, or read, or go out, or prepare to go to sleep. But you must not masturbate or engage in any sexual relations for at least one hour.

While going about your normal routine after this ritual, your sexual drive will be very strong. Whenever you feel a need to masturbate or have sexual relations in any form, repeat the Control Mantra and use the yantra imagery to maintain your Control.

If, after one hour has passed, you engage in any form of sex, you will find that, having completed the Control Ritual, your sexual energy is increased. You will reach a higher level of sexual stimulation and greater, more intense, satisfaction. Enjoy the increase in your sexual pleasure; right now you don't need to be concerned with Tantric Control.

The first time you try this exercise will be the most difficult. Each succeeding time, you will find Control comes a little more easily. After a while you will be able to draw closer and closer to the actual point of orgasm, and still be able to pull back with Tantric Control. The stronger your Control becomes, the better. It is not considered unusual, once complete Control is established, to continue masturbating while the mantra and yantra imagery of control are used. You will then be able to sustain yourself on the verge of orgasm indefinitely, while controlling it completely. This of course comes only with time and regular practice of the Awareness and Control exercises.

Initiates often ask whether this Control Ritual should be performed nightly as an extension of the Focusing and Intensifying Focus Rituals. The answer is *yes*. Just as the Awareness Rituals are part of establishing a daily pattern, so this all-important Control Ritual must be part of the conditioning process. To be able to heighten Awareness, pleasure, and Control, the patterns must be established and practiced regularly.

Now you are beginning to see that these rituals proceed in a logical sequence designed to gradually bring heightened sexual pleasure, while enabling you to have control over it.

This is the most important single ritual of the Tantra. It may appear to be the most difficult to master, but if you follow the instructions carefully and practice with determination, mindful of the objectives to be gained, you will soon master it.

Now we move on to a logical extension of this Control Ritual: The Channeling of Sexual Power.

CHANNELING POWER AND ENERGY

The Tantra tells this story of the "first humans" brought forth by Kali and Mahakala:

All were Tantric Masters at the beginning. They multiplied and initiated all into the knowledge and pleasures of Tantra. But succeeding generations became so engrossed in pleasure, they lost the knowledge of using their sexual energy for creative purposes in their lives.

Each Tantrik was a master of pleasure and Control, to heighten pleasure. But the regenerated power and energy filled them with anxiety, for they had no purpose for it beyond that of pleasure.

The Tantra tells the story of that Tantric Master who heightened sensitivity and pleasure each day, but could not find the key for channeling this great energy to other parts of her being. The search itself caused great frustration. She became nervous and unhappy— even amid the sensual pleasures she experienced.

Then, one night, as she held her lover in her arms and drew pleasure, her mind, emotions, and body reeled with a vision; she was enveloped by the duality of Kali and Mahakala. They fired her body to such heights of ecstasy that she entered a trance-like state, on the verge of an orgasm that would not occur because Kali repeatedly wrote the yantra of Control on her mind while Mahakala entered her from below and whispered the mantra of Control into her ear.

Suspended between the taut heights of pleasures and control, she suddenly heard a new mantra from Mahakala, while Kali pictured on the blackness of her mind all of the practical everyday things which the woman desired in life.

Suddenly the Kali and Mahakala were gone, but they had bestowed on this Tantric Master the great secret of Tantra: Controlled Channeling.

She had relearned the secret which had become lost. And she taught the secret to her lover, and to all those who would learn. And she worshiped Kali and Mahakala, and founded anew the great cult of ecstasy known as Tantra.

The Channeling Mantra

The sound: *Ahh. Nahh. Yahh. Tawnnn.*

The Channeling Ritual

You have established the nightly ritual of Awareness, through the Focusing and Intensifying Focus Rituals, and carried these through to the Control Ritual. You have reached the point where you are on the verge of orgasm. You remove your hands and cease masturbation. You are bringing about Control through the use of the Control Mantra and Yantra.

Your hands are folded across your abdomen and you are still in the same position on the bed, nude, knees apart, soles of feet pressed together.

Through the Control Mantra and Yantra, you have reached a point where you feel you have attained Control; you have stopped the impending orgasm and, though you would *like* to continue masturbating or have sex relations, you will not because you are in Control and will not violate the One-Hour rule.

When you reach this point, you may begin the rewarding Tantric process of Channeling.

This is the procedure:

When you have attained Control, retain your position and cease the Control Mantra and Yantra. You may resume them, of course, if the urgent desire for sexual satisfaction overtakes you.

Now, fix in your mind the image of some everyday situation or problem that has been bothering you. You may have decided, prior to beginning, precisely what problem or situation you will choose for Channeling.

Suppose you have a serious problem to solve, or a decision to make, or suppose you have been irritable and nervous. Start thinking about the problem as soon as you attain Control. Isolate it. Start saying the Channeling Mantra over and over, while "writing" the words identifying the problem, on the black void of imagery.

This will begin a conditioning process that channels your highly stimulated sexual concentration into the resolution of the problem.

The process is deceptively simple:

You have attained Control.

You are ready to Channel your energy.

You retain your position on the bed and start saying the Channeling Mantra over and over, alternating it with an isolated statement of the problem, as follows:

"Ahh. Nahhh. Yahh. Tawnnn. I will remain more calm and patient. Be at peace within myself and with others. *Ahh. Nahh. Yahh. Tawnnn."*

Or:

"Ahh. Nahh. Yahh. Tawnnn. The right idea for solving the problem about ———— will come to me. I am creative. The answer will come. *Ahh. Nahh. Yahh. Tawnnn."*

Repeat the process six times, presenting the same problem or desire each of the six times. Keep the wording simple, and repeat it. Your mind already *knows* the *details* of the problem, so all you want is a few words to direct concentration to it. To intensify that concentration, "write" the words you are saying to yourself (mantra included) on the black void of imagery.

Once you have repeated the Channeling six times, cease the Channeling Mantra and stop thinking about the problem or the process.

Now recite the Control Mantra two times.

Then repeat twice the Awareness Mantra. Remove your hands from your stomach and get up from the bed.

Now, observing the One-Hour Rule, go about your

regular routine. Many Tantriks perform the Awareness, Control, and Channeling Rituals about one to two hours before they go to bed to sleep. They arise after the exercise, have a glass of wine, take a hot bath, and then, after the hour has passed, go to bed, prepared for sex or just for sleep.

You will still be in a sexually stimulated state. Use the Control Mantra, along with the Control imagery, to maintain Control during the One Hour, or longer, if you wish.

Do not expect the answer or solution to the problem you presented during Channeling to suddenly pop into your mind. Try not to dwell on it. Your ally, your sexual concentrative power, is now subconsciously at work for you.

At some unexpected moment, the answer will surface. Or you will realize that the desired results are being achieved.

And with each passing night of practicing the Awareness, Control, and Channeling Rituals, all of your powers will increase.

COUPLES' RITUALS: THE SEVEN NIGHTS OF THE TANTRA

PREFACE

The Seven Nights of the Tantra are the classic rituals of Tantric study. First, through the senses of your partner, you will develop a new Awareness of your own sexuality as well as a new Awareness of your partner. And in the process of this new Awareness you will learn to overcome false modesty and inhibitions, and experience new openness and honesty in sex.

Then the nights become Nights of Control. These Rituals not only bring Control itself, but also develop a deep communication between the Male and the Female as they strive together to reach new plateaus of ecstasy.

If possible, the rituals of the Seven Nights of the Tantra should be done on seven consecutive nights. However, this is not essential. They could be done every other night for two weeks—or over an even longer period. But for the best results, they should be done in as short a time span as possible. And they must be done in the order set forth.

What if, on a given Night of the Tantra, control is lost and orgasm occurs? What happens then?

In such a case—which does happen—the best solution is to stop the ritual and invoke the One-Hour Rule. After waiting an hour, begin the ritual again, from the beginning.

If you are not happy with the way one night's ritual has gone, you may repeat it the following night.

One of the primary objects in these Rituals is to

form a bond of uninhibited commitment and communication between the partners. You should read together the Rituals' instructions before beginning, and discuss every aspect of them.

Ecstasy itself, heightened enjoyment of love through sexual expression, is achieved in the Seven Nights of the Tantra. The ever-present goal of increased power through Channeling is also a part of each night's ritual.

The One-Hour Rule, emphasized again and again, is observed in the Seven Nights. During this one hour of extremely heightened sexual energy the channeling process is most effective. This hour now becomes part of the ritual itself, adding not only to the power of Channeling, but further heightening Awareness, Control, and pleasure.

The rituals themselves should be followed explicitly. Some portions will be more difficult than others. The meaning and purpose of some of the instructions may not be immediately obvious, but they should be followed precisely if they are to accomplish their purpose.

Do not ignore or "skip over" even the most basic instruction. Between couples there is often a reaction of "But I know what I look like" or "We've done something like this before; let's do it our way." These are the pitfalls the Tantric texts warn against. One of the oldest texts says: "Let the man or woman who knows, teach; let those who have not reached the highest plateau, learn."

The meaning is clear.

It is essential that you master the basic Female and Male Rituals before beginning the Couples' ritual. The developers of the Tantra, being as human as we are, were aware that the student of Tantra would desire to "rush" the basic Male and Female Rituals in order to get to the Couples' Rituals. For this reason, repetition of the basic Rituals is included as a part of the Couples' Rituals. A most important part.

In "sharing" the basic Rituals the couples will reach a deeper Awareness and Understanding of each other. Simultaneously, all inhibitions about your own or your partner's body or sexuality will be overcome.

The Food

During these nights the Tantric texts recommend certain foods. All the texts refer to the couple having "cheese, wine, and bread" within reach, prepared prior to the beginning of each evening. Just why these three items of food, the texts do not explain. Probably simply because of their easy availability, and rather universal appeal. Being realistic, the repast during that hour might just as well be champagne and caviar, or beer and pretzels. This is one of the few areas where the Tantrik can make his and her own decisions.

The Lights

The lighting in the rooms used for the Couples' Exercises is very important.

The Tantric texts specify "a place with four lanterns lit if daylight be absent." This can be interpreted in modern terms as "at least two lamps, with a minimum of sixty-watts each."

In the Meeting Room with the low table, where the Couples' Rituals begin, the lamps may be placed a bit away from the table, with one or more candles on the table itself. Even in the Meeting Room the sense of sight plays an important part, so the lamps must be on.

In the bedroom, the sense of sight is extremely important. At least two sixty-watt lamps must be on, preferably one on a small table at the head of the bed and the second on a table at the foot of the bed.

However it is done, the lights must not be put out. Remember: "Tantra abhors darkness."

Now enter into the Cult of Ecstasy with anticipation of the pleasure in store for you.

THE FIRST NIGHT OF THE TANTRA

The Tantric Master brought them together, Male and Female, the First Night of the Tantra.

And the Master spoke:

"You have made your commitment to each other by your presence. You shall know the ecstasy of Kali and Mahakala as you move upward in search of the perfect union which transcends all and brings true enlightenment."

And the Tantric Master guided them, each and together, through the ritual:

Ideally two rooms should be used: one with a couch and low coffee table with pillows around it; the second, a bedroom. A single room makes it difficult when the Ritual specifies that the couple be separated for one purpose or another. However, this problem can be overcome, possibly by one partner or the other waiting in the bath or kitchen while the other follows the instructions (thus the partners take turns with portions of the ritual, rather than completing them simultaneously in adjoining rooms.)

There should always be a bottle of wine, bread, and cheese, or whatever alternative repast the couple has chosen.

On the First Night of the Tantra, the couple should sit beside each other on the pillows beside the coffee table. Pour and drink one glass of wine each, but do not touch one another except as instructed.

While having your wine, this night and all other nights, you should determine what goals you will seek through the Channeling that will occur later. These need not be discussed, unless you wish to reveal your Channeling goals to each other.

When the glass of wine is drunk, lean forward and kiss gently on the lips, then part. The Male should now stand and say, "I am ready." (This is a direct translation from ancient Tantric Texts. It communicates that you are ready to proceed to the next phase of the ritual, or, in later procedures, that both partners are ready and willing to enter into the planned ritual, whatever it may be.) The Female should then stand in front of him. The Male remains absolutely passive, his arms down by his sides, as the Female undresses him, beginning with his shoes, socks, trousers, sweater, shirt, and underwear. As she removes each item, she should look at, but not touch, that part of his body she has uncovered. And she should repeat the Awareness Mantra, barely audibly, as each item is removed. Thus she will overcome any self-consciousness about verbalizing the mantra in front of her partner.

Once the Male is totally nude, the Female should stand in front of him and say, "I am ready." The Male now removes her garments, beginning with her shoes, stockings, skirt or slacks, sweater or blouse or shirt,

bra, and underpants. He should likewise say, barely
audibly, the Awareness Mantra as he removes each item
and stares at the area of her body he has uncovered.

Now the two stand facing each other.

The Male now proceeds with the basic steps of the
Awareness Ritual, except that rather than focusing on
his own reflection in a mirror, he will focus on the Female's image in front of him. The Female remains passive as the Male says the Awareness Mantra and extends his fingers and thumbs to touch her lips; then to
touch the nipple of each breast; then to touch her
abdomen, then to slide his hands downward to her
abdomen, through the pubic hair, to rest on the pubic
bone. At each point, he repeats the Awareness Mantra
and focuses his gaze and concentration on the parts being touched.

The Male then drops his arms to his sides and
closes his eyes tightly, forming an image of the Female
in his mind (just as he formed his own mirror image).
With his eyes still closed, he extends his thumbs and
index fingers toward the Female. She, with her eyes
open, guides his hands first to her lips, then to each
nipple, then to the abdomen, then to the mons veneris.
She pauses at each point until she has heard him say
the Awareness Mantra and knows he is ready to proceed to the next point.

The ritual should proceed slowly, so that each partner may enjoy touching and being touched.

After the Male has rested his hands on the mons
veneris, the Female releases his hands, which he returns to his sides, and he opens his eyes. He will have
held in his mind, while his eyes were closed, the image
and sensory impression of each part of her body he
touched.

Then the Female begins the process by staring at the Male's body as she did her own mirror image in the Awareness Ritual. She stares and concentrates as she moves her hands (index fingers and thumbs) to the Male's lips; then to each nipple; then to his abdomen; then, sliding both thumbs and index fingers downward along the abdomen, through the pubic hair, to encircle the penis just at its base and exert a slight "squeezing" pressure. At each point, she stops long enough to say the Awareness Mantra.

The Male remains passive.

Then the Female drops her hands to her sides. She stares at the Male, then closes her eyes tight, to form an image of the Male clearly in her mind. She then extends her index fingers and thumbs to him. The Male, eyes open, takes her hands and directs the thumbs and index fingers to his lips; then to each nipple; then to the abdomen; then downward on the abdomen to the base of the penis, which is encircled and "squeezed" as before. The Male holds the Female's hands at each point until he has heard her say one Awareness Mantra. The Female keeps her eyes closed, while holding in her mind the yantra image and sensory impression of each part of the Male's body she is touching.

Now embrace, then part and sit across the table from each other. Sit quietly for a moment, then join both hands across the table and say one Awareness Mantra. At this point there should be no conversation.

Now you must separate, each to a different room; or each in turn leaving the room.

Once she is in a room alone, the Female assumes the Awareness Ritual position, nude, on her back, soles pressed together, and goes through the Awareness Rituals, proceeding to the Control Ritual.

In another room, the Male likewise performs the Awareness Rituals, then the Control Ritual.

It is mandatory that these rituals be performed alone. Try not to be distracted by the knowledge that your partner is in the next room doing the same thing. Particularly in the Control Ritual, it may be extremely difficult to prevent yourself from calling out to your partner to come to you while you are verging on orgasm. It is precisely this increased sexual stimulation requiring increased Control that is necessary to achieve the Tantric goal.

The Male and Female, each alone, proceed to the end of the Control Ritual and once having come to the threshold of orgasm, then having attained Control, each spends a few minutes reinforcing that Control and doing the Channeling Ritual.

Once you have each finished the Channeling Ritual, begin repeating the Control Mantra again, aloud. This is done to help retain Control under hyperstimulating circumstances. It also lets your partner know that you have completed the Channeling Ritual.

When both partners have heard the other saying the Control Mantra loudly, one will say "I am ready." Do not move from the position of the Ritual until your partner has replied, "I am ready." Then rise from your positions and meet again at the low table. This moment will require great Control. Both of you have been stimulated to the point of orgasm, and you'll be fighting for Control. Of course, you will be obviously aware of your partner's arousal; the penis remains erect, or partially erect; the nipples may also be flushed and erect, the clitoris and labia distended.

Pour two glasses of wine, sit across from each other at the table, join hands and repeat the Control Mantra. Then sip the wine, without conversation.

You should repeat, as loudly and as often as necessary, the Control Mantra, in order to maintain absolute control.

The Channeling Mantra should be used during the next hour. It will be most effective in this charged air of sexual excitement and energy.

When either the Female or the Male feels the attainment of complete control and has used the Channeling process, you may begin to speak to each other. You may discuss your feelings and the Ritual, or anything you wish, but you must not touch.

If you feel Control slipping away, repeat the Control Mantra—and the all-important Control Yantra imagery. Remember, the Control imagery works best, whether alone or in the Couples' situations, when you say the mantra and at the same time "write" the words of the Mantra in large white letters on the black void of imagery. By imagining the letters forming the words of the mantra, the mind doubles its concentration on the Control Yantra image and Mantra, and Control comes easier, faster.

Now, the wine and cheese and bread. And talk. A time for intimate verbal communication during this entire hour.

When the hour has passed—and it must be an hour, not fifty minutes—you may do whatever you wish. Have sexual relations in whatever manner you wish, without concern for anything other than the ecstasy of loving, being loved, and feeling fulfilled and satisfied.

After having sexual relations, you should know that, though your body is going through the postcoital period of satiation called "resolution," there remains within you a fantastic supply of sexual energy and concentrative force. This can best be utilized, as you go to sleep, by using the Channeling Mantra and Yantra imagery, to help you achieve other goals in your life.

"In this way are you joined beyond your physical union, beyond pleasure, beyond time, as one."

THE SECOND NIGHT OF THE TANTRA

The Tantric Master spoke to the Female and Male:

"No secret part of your physical self shall you keep hidden from one another. You shall look upon the body of the other as your own; upon the mind of the other, as your own; upon the yantra and mantra of the other, as your own; upon the pleasure of the other, as your own.

"Seek to know even the smallest part of the other, and share the smallest part of yourself. Therein lie the pleasures and the powers that can be yours."

As on the First Night, the wine and food should be set on the low table and you should sit beside each other on pillows, at the table. One glass of wine for each should be poured and sipped as you discuss the Ritual and plan the Channeling that you will use later.

On this night it is the Female's turn to stand first and say "I am ready."

The male undresses her as on the first night, repeating the Awareness Mantra as he removes each item of clothing until she is totally nude.

Then the Male remains passive, arms at sides, and says, "I am ready," and the Female undresses him, saying the Awareness Mantra as each article of clothing is removed, until he is completely nude.

At this point, the Female and Male face each other, and perform the previous night's adaptation of the "mirror" Awareness Ritual, first with eyes open, then with eyes closed.

The partners then step close to each other, encircle each other with their arms, and kiss, long and probingly—but with no stimulation other than the kiss itself and the closeness of the bodies embracing.

The Couple should then walk nude to the bathroom. A hot, steaming tub of water should be drawn. A shower may be used but Tantric texts specify the tub (river) bath.

The Male seats himself in the tub of water. The Female, kneeling at the side of the tub, washes his shoulders, back and chest. The Male then rises to a kneeling position in the tub and the Female washes his genitals. She should not attempt to sexually stimulate the genitals. The washing action itself, with soap and cloth, then rinsing, will prove stimulating enough.

The Male should then step from the tub and the Female should dry his body with a warm towel. Here again there should be no additional caressing of the genitals.

Now, depending upon the individuals' wishes, a new tub of water may be drawn, or the same water used. The Female sits in the bath, the Male kneeling beside the tub. He washes her back, shoulders, and breasts. Then the Female rises to a kneeling position in the tub and the Male washes her genitals. The Male should not attempt any extra genital stimulation.

The Female then steps from the tub and the Male dries her with a warm towel.

The intimacy of the bath will heighten once more the Awareness of each other's bodies and will help remove any inhibitions between the partners.

The Tantric texts carry this "removal of modesty" a step further by stating that if either of the partners desires to urinate prior to getting into the tub of water, it should be done in full view of the other partner. Viewing yet another normal function of the partner's body will not only heighten intimacy but, more important, will enable the partners to overcome self-consciousness in allowing others to witness moments usually regarded as personal and solitary.

Now the couple, their bath completed, walk nude to the room and sit at the low table.

Now, as on the first night, you separate, each to a different room. Again, go through the Awareness Rituals, then proceed to the Control Ritual. When orgasm is impending, fight for Control through the Control Mantra and Control Yantra imagery, until Control is attained. Then proceed to your individual Channeling Ritual. Once Control is complete and the Channeling Ritual done, let your partner know with the words "I am ready." When you both have said this (and it must never be said until the Channeling is complete), get up and meet again at the low table. As it was last night, Control may be difficult, but it must be maintained. By now you should be able to help each other by holding hands and repeating the Control Mantra together. The "writing" of the words of the Control Mantra onto the yantra image remains the *key* to attaining and holding onto Control.

The Channeling Mantra is repeated as often as desired in this atmosphere of charged sexual energy and power. And the wine is drunk, the repast eaten.

On this night the Tantra permits a slight reduction to the One-Hour Rule, for a purpose.

When *forty-five minutes* have passed, move the pillows away from the low table. Assume a seated position opposite each other. The Female should raise her knees while seated on the pillow, then spread her feet and knees as far apart as is comfortable for her.

The Male should raise his knees and sit so that his legs are across the Female's thighs, his feet are on either side of the Female's buttocks. Thus their knees should be fairly close; her right knee to his left, his right knee to her left.

This is known as "The Contemplative Position of Tantra."

Their hands should rest on each other's kneecaps. In this Contemplative Position, the genitals are open to view, yet the bodies are slightly separated.

Begin to say softly the Awareness Mantra. Look first at each other's faces, then at the nipples of the breasts, then at the navel, and finally at the penis or vagina.

Without moving, each should look at and concentrate on the genitals of the other. The Awareness Mantra should be said twice. Then the partners should close their eyes and bring to their minds the imagery of the other partner's sex organs. At this point, the yantra imagery should become more vivid and the imagination should create pictures of the partner.

The Female should imagine the Male's organ erect and growing across the space between them, stimulating her clitoris and penetrating her vagina.

The Male should imagine the Female's vagina opening and taking his penis deep within her.

Once this imagery has been attained, the partners should begin the Control Mantra and open their eyes.

The imagery will bring on a resurgence of sexual stimulation. Maintain the position, without moving, through three recitations of the Control Mantra while looking at the other's genitals. Then close your eyes and use the Channeling Mantra and Imagery.

At this point, rise and embrace, and go together to bed, to make love as you wish, with total abandon and joy. Enjoy the heightened arousal this ritual has brought. Give to each other all the pleasure desired and you will receive pleasure and satisfaction.

When your lovemaking is finished, and you lie close to sleep, do not forget, as you fall asleep, that powerful energy forces are still at work within your subconscious mind. Make use of them. Go off to sleep as the great Tantric Masters do—using the Channeling Mantra and Yantra imagery to lull you to sleep, while putting your energy forces to work for the night.

THE THIRD NIGHT OF THE TANTRA

The Tantric Master spoke:
"Female and Male draw their joy from the centers of pleasure each comprehends within the other. Each serves the other, gives to the other. Then in turn each is served and received. And thus the chain of pleasure is unbroken; the energy created, magnified; the power over the universe, attained.

"In ritualistic praise to Kali shall the Male seek to Control his great powers for pleasure as he devotes his mind and body to giving pleasure to the Female.

"Likewise, in ritualistic form as praise to Mahakala, shall the Female Control all energy and capacity for unlimited pleasure with herself and devote her mind and body to bringing pleasure to the Male."

Again the repast is set on the low table and you drink one glass of wine each, and contemplate the Ritual and the Channeling of the evening.

When he has finished his glass of wine, the Male stands near the Female, who remains seated. The Male says, "I am ready." The Female stays where she is and watches as the Male undresses himself. He removes each piece of clothing slowly, until he is standing completely nude before her.

Facing his partner, the Male now closes his eyes tightly, his arms by his sides. He now begins, alone, the Awakening Ritual, his fingertips to his lips, then relaxing his arms; then bringing the fingertips to apply pressure to each nipple in turn; then resting the fingertips on his abdomen and sliding them downward to the base of the penis, which he encircles with the fingers, and applying Awareness pressure ("squeezing"). Then he relaxes his hands and lets them hang at his sides. Eyes closed, the Male holds the imagery of his actions in his mind, and says the Awareness Mantra as he touches each part of his body.

The Female watches each movement intently, paying careful attention to the manner in which the Male applies the Awareness pressure to each part of his body.

Then the Male sits.

The Female now stands and says, "I am ready." Then she undresses, removing each garment slowly. The Male watches from his seated position.

When the Female is standing nude in front of the Male, she faces him and closes her eyes tightly. Now she begins the Awakening Ritual, touching her fingers first to her lips; then bringing the fingers to each breast and nipple; then bringing the fingers to her abdomen, and slowly sliding them down the abdomen to exert Awareness pressure on the vagina.

At each point, the Female pauses long enough to say the Awareness Mantra once; and during the entire ritual she holds the yantra imagery of her actions firmly in mind.

By the time this ritual is attempted, both partners should have used the Awakening Ritual often enough that they can go through the ritual slowly, holding the image and saying the mantra, without hesitation. There should be little or no self-consciousness about it with the partner watching. Indeed, that is part of the purpose of this portion of the exercise: to remove any remnants of self-consciousness or inhibition between the partners, as well as adding a new dimension to their Awareness.

When the Female has finished the Awakening Ritual, the Male stands beside her. They face each other and embrace, then kiss; the touching of their lips and their bodies is the only contact between them.

Now, as on the previous night, they proceed to the bath.

The Tantric texts are explicit about the bathing process as a part of these exercises. But the emphasis is on the bathing of the genitals (hips and anus included), and the bathing of the breasts. An entire "bath" is not necessarily required.

For example, the tub may be filled one-third full and the Male and Female alternately kneel in the warm water, while the other partner washes breasts and genitals with a warm soapy cloth, then rinses the areas washed, drying off the partner when she or he steps from the tub. Or you may take a shower together, each in turn washing the other, then drying one another. Or, if a bidet is available, one partner at a time may straddle the bidet and the other wash his or her genitals, then dry them.

Any of these variations of the bath will serve equally well, provided you wash and dry *each other*.

After the bath, walk *together* to the bedroom.

Be sure to remember that the bedroom is to be adequately lighted. Tantra abhors darkness and the loss of visual sense and sensation.

Embrace for a moment, then the Male should lie on the bed, assuming the position used for Awareness Rituals: knees apart, soles of feet together, hands folded across the abdomen.

The Female should sit passively at the foot of the bed, if possible in a position just below the Male's feet, so that she can watch without having to move.

The Female should pay quiet, concentrated attention to each movement made by the Male, noting particularly the precise manner in which he touches himself as he proceeds.

The Male should close his eyes tightly, and begin by saying the Awareness Mantra to himself, while fixing in his mind a vivid image of himself, as he always does during this exercise.

Do not rush. The image must be firmly fixed; then the Male may begin as follows:

First fold your hands across your stomach at navel level. Slowly move your hands to touch your lips, yantra imagery and mantra fixed in the mind, for this and all other movements. Then your hands return to the abdomen. Next, the index fingers and thumbs move to the nipples of each breast, rolling the nipple slightly. Once again your hands return to the abdomen, then move down the abdomen through the pubic hair, encircling the penis and squeezing the base of the penis.

Now, return the hands to the abdomen, say the Awareness Mantra three times while relaxing, then repeat the Ritual. This is a deviation from the Focusing Ritual, where usually the second phase is only the imagery of repetition. This time actually move the fingers and thumbs to the lips, nipples, abdomen, and penis again.

After pressure is applied to the penis the second time, relax your hands but keep them on the penis, saying the mantra again as the index fingers move downward, following the outline of the penis to its deepest perceptible base, within the scrotum, exerting just enough pressure for pleasure.

Relax your hands, then slide them downward, until the index fingers come to the perineum, where pressure is exerted. Relax the hands again, and slide the fingertips across the perineum to the rectal muscles, and apply inward pressure.

Then return the hands to the base of the penis, encircle it, and apply pressure.

Then return the hands to the abdomen and relax. Repeat Three Awareness Mantras. Then open your eyes and sit up.

At this point there should be no discussion of the ritual. Concentration on the ritual itself should be of prime importance.

The Male now rises from the bed. The Female rises and they embrace for a silent moment.

Now the Female lies on the bed, assuming the same position: hands folded across abdomen, knees apart, soles of feet pressed together.

The eyes are to be closed tightly, the mantra repeated, and the yantra imagery of herself firmly established before proceeding. There should be no rush. Each facet of imagery must be attained before the rituals begin.

The Male sits passively, quietly, at the foot of the bed.

Once the Female has attained her imagery, she should continue the Mantra and proceed by bringing fingers to lips, then returning the hands to their position on the abdomen.

Bring the fingers to the breasts, then upward on the breasts to the nipples, touching and "rolling" the nipples in a pleasingly sensual manner, then returning the hands to the abdomen.

Now slide the hands slowly down the abdomen, through the pubic hair, across the mons veneris, to rest on the vagina. The thumbs then slowly part the labia and the fingers exert pressure on the clitoris. Return the hands to the abdomen and say the Awareness Mantra three times.

Then, rather than the second phase of doing the ritual in imagery alone, the ritual is repeated physically; fingers to lips; then to nipples, rolling them; then to abdomen, down across the mons veneris to the vagina, thumbs parting the vaginal labia, fingers exerting pressure on the clitoris.

Now, do not return your hands to your abdomen. Rather, allow them to relax on the vagina. Then slide the index fingers downward until they touch and exert pressure on the perineum. Then return your hands to the vagina, open the labia and exert pressure on the clitoris. Again relax the hands, resting them on your vagina.

Say one Awareness Mantra and slide the hands across

the perineum, to exert inward presure on the rectal
muscles. Then bring the hands to rest on the vagina,
open the labia, and apply pressure to the clitoris. Then
return the hands to their crossed position on the abdomen.

Repeat three Awareness Mantras, and then open your
eyes and sit up.

Without speaking, the Female and Male should embrace for only a moment and walk together from the
bedroom to the low table in the Meeting Room.

As you sit across from each other, say the Awareness Mantra.

Then separate, go into different rooms, and lie once
again in the Awareness position.

Then, separately, as you have just done in each
other's presence, go through the Awareness Rituals and
proceed as on previous nights to the Control Ritual,
stimulating yourself to the verge of orgasm, and Controlling the orgasm to prevent its occurring.

Once Control is attained, use the Channeling Mantra
and go through the Channeling Ritual.

When the Channeling Rituals have been completed,
each partner will say, "I am aready," and when *both* of
you have voiced this, rise and return to the table.

At the low table note the time, then sit and drink
and have your repast. As necessary, use the Control
Mantra and Control Yantra imagery to maintain Control.

Use the Channeling Mantra and Yantra imagery to
reinforce the Channeling you have begun.

Following the ritual of the Third Night, observe the
One-Hour Rule, as you maintain your Control and use
your Channeling, enjoy your food and drink, and converse with each other.

When forty-five minutes have passed, sit opposite each other in the Contemplative Position of Tantra— the Female's knees raised, feet flat on the floor, legs apart. The Male moves into the position, his knees raised; his feet resting on either side of her buttocks; your hands resting on each other's kneecaps.

In this Contemplative Position, concentrate on each others' genitals, while repeating two times the mantra of Awareness.

Once the mantra is finished, the Male should say, "I am ready."

The Female removes her hands from the Male's kneecaps and leans forward from the pelvis, extending her right and left hands to the Male's genitals. Keeping her palms up, she rests the index finger and thumb of each hand on either side of the base of the penis and scrotum. Slide the index fingers downward, until they are under the base of the scrotum, then close the thumbs around the top of the penis, close the palms of your hands, and cup the penis and testicles within your hands. Apply pressure, holding the organs only tightly enough to be aware of their presence in your hands.

Still holding the penis and testicles in her hands the female says, "I am ready."

When she says this, the Male repeats the Awareness Mantra as he contracts the muscles of his groin in the manner set forth in the Yantric Body exercise. He should perform the muscular contractions just as he does when alone. While contracting the muscles, he says the Awareness Mantra again, and closes his eyes tightly, forming the imagery of muscular contraction, the "tubes," and the "filling" as specified. His eyes remain closed.

Then he relaxes the muscles. The movement of the

contraction along with the imagery should be very noticeable to the Female, who says, "I feel." The Male does *not* open his eyes.

The Male then repeats the muscular tightening, imagery, and mantra, holding the contraction as long as is comfortable.

Again the Female says, "I feel."

And a third time the Male contracts the muscles, while holding the imagery, his eyes still closed, and saying the mantra for the third time. He then relaxes the muscles again.

And the Female says, "I feel." She then relaxes the index fingers from beneath the scrotum and slides them upward, so that her fingers and thumbs are encircling the penis at the base. Thus she exerts slightly more squeezing pressure and slowly pulls her hands, still encircling the penis, away from the Male's body, along the shaft of the penis, to the tip. She then returns her hands to the Male's kneecaps. At this point the Male will have an erection. If he is aroused to the point of distraction, he should repeat the Control Mantra aloud, so that the Female will know to wait for him to attain Control.

Only the actions specified are to be done by the Female. She should do no additional fondling, stroking, or massaging and handling of any kind.

Now the Couple both say the Control Mantra twice, to reinforce their control. The Female says, "I am ready." She sits passively, her hands on the Male's kneecaps, her eyes closed tight.

The Male now moves his right hand from her kneecap and leans forward from the pelvis.

His right hand moves slowly to the Female's vagina. His right thumb and index finger part the labia, making a conscious effort not to touch or stimulate the clitoris. Once the labia are parted, slowly and gently insert the right index into the vagina, the palm of the hand up, the thumb and other fingers balled into a "fist," out of the way. The Male holds his finger perfectly still and concentrates on feeling the "pressure" of the vaginal muscles.

With the finger in place, the Male says, "I am ready."

The Female then proceeds with the imagery of this ritual, as when it is performed alone. Holding this imagery, she says the Awareness Mantra while contracting the vaginal muscles. Then she relaxes the muscles.

The Male says, "I feel," as he does indeed feel the vaginal muscles move against his finger.

A second time the muscles are contracted, the imagery reinforced, and the mantra said; then the contraction is relaxed after being held as long as possible.

When the Female relaxes, the Male again says, "I feel."

A third muscular tightening is now done—the contraction held as long as possible, the imagery maintained, the mantra said.

When the third contraction is finished, the Female relaxes.

Slowly the Male begins to pull his finger from the vagina, exerting a slight upward pressure. As you do this, slide your finger from the vagina, upward across the urethral opening and across the clitoris. Then without hesitation, again place your right hand on you partner's kneecap.

It should be clear that if, at any point in this part of the ritual, either partner feels overwhelmingly aroused, she or he should begin immediately to say the Control Mantra and concentrate totally on the Control imagery.

By performing this ritual in the Contemplative Position, after the solitary Control Rituals have been com-

pleted, and the One Hour (almost) has passed, the
ritual furthers Awareness; the muscular contractions
of the ritual are "shared"; and another aspect of Control, the key to Tantra, is achieved.

After this Contemplative Ritual is completed, the
couple should retire to bed, to enjoy each other and
their increasing Awareness of each other, without
thought of anything but their own pleasure.

And, once again, when sleep is upon you, you should
ease into the restoring pleasure of sleep with the Channeling Mantra and Channeling Yantra imagery, using
the great storehouse of energy and concentration you
have gathered to work for you while the body rests in
sleep.

THE FOURTH NIGHT OF THE TANTRA

Though the Tantric Master may not be physically
present during the Seven Nights of the Tantra, his or
her presence is felt as the rituals are carried out.

The Tantric Master speaks to the mind, emotions,
body, and spirit.

The Bond of Tantra is formed between the Female
and Male through the rituals. As the Tantric Master
says:

*"Ask not that others understand the joining of your
bodies in pleasure, nor your minds in comprehension,
nor your spirits in understanding. They who have not
experienced, cannot know. Seek not to explain, for
words will fail you.*

"Open instead your bodies, minds, feelings, and

spirits only to those who have shared the experience of the rituals. They will understand. And your sharing of knowledge through exchange of words with other Tantriks can serve to create further understanding within yourself."

In this ritual, the setting is the same as on the previous nights. The Couple meets at the table and drinks the first glass of wine while contemplating this ritual and the subject of their Channeling.

When the glass of wine has been drunk, the Male stands, says, "I am ready," and slowly removes his clothes as the Female watches. Then the Male sits and the Female stands, says, "I am ready," and removes her clothes slowly. The procedure is to be followed precisely as it was the previous night.

Now totally nude, stand facing each other, kiss and embrace, then walk to the bath.

The procedure of the bath is to be followed, using the tub, shower, or bidet.

Then return again to the table and sit quietly for a few minutes.

Then once again assume the Contemplative Position of Tantra. With your hands on each others' kneecaps, say three mantras of Awareness.

Then the Male says, "I am ready." The Female moves her hands from his knees and leans forward from the pelvis, to grasp and "cup" the Male's penis and testicles as she did in last night's Contemplative portion of the ritual.

Once the Male's genitals are cupped within her hands, encircled by her fingers, the Female says, "I am ready."

The Male then proceeds with the ritual. He is to follow the procedure precisely as he did last night: three contractions, with the Female saying, "I feel," as each contraction is relaxed. Then, at the end of the third contraction, the Female slides her hands, fingers, and thumbs encircling the penis with pressure, away from the Male's body, along the shaft of the penis, to the glans. She then releases the penis and returns her hands to his knees.

After saying three mantras, the Female says, "I am ready," and the Male removes his right hand from her knee, leaning forward from the pelvis, inserting his right index finger slowly into her vagina, following precisely the same procedure as before.

Once the index finger is in place in the vagina, and the other fingers of his hand are "curled" to prevent their touching the outer areas of the vagina, the Male says, "I am ready."

Now the Female contracts the muscles three times, relaxing after each contraction, at which point the Male says, "I feel."

At the end of the third contraction, the Male slowly withdraws his finger, with a slight upward pressure so that, as it is withdrawn, the finger wipes upward, across the urethra and clitoris, then away from the vagina and back to its place on her knee.

Once again the couple is reminded that the use of fewer words, in describing a ritual when it is repeated, does not diminish the importance of the ritual, nor the importance of carrying out that ritual in *every detail*.

Once this is completed, the couple should return to the table and remain silent for a minute, directing their attention to the mantra and the remaining parts of this ritual.

They stand, embrace, kiss, and walk to the bedroom.

In the lighted bedroom, the Male lies on his back

on the bed, in the Awareness-Control position, hands folded across abdomen, knees apart, soles of feet pressing together. He closes his eyes and establishes the imagery of himself, while saying the Awareness Mantra.

The Female sits at the foot of the bed, just beyond the Male's feet. During this ritual she should not move and she is not to touch the Male, or herself.

The Male now begins the Awareness Ritual with some modification, as follows:

He brings his hands from his abdomen to his lips, holds the yantra image, says the mantra, and returns hands to abdomen.

He brings his hands to his nipples, says the mantra, rolls the nipples with pleasing pressure, holds the imagery, repeats the mantra, then returns his hands to his abdomen.

He slides his hands downward across his abdomen, through the pubic hair, to the base of the penis. His fingers and thumbs 'surround the base of the penis and squeeze while he holds the imagery and says the mantra twice.

His fingers slide along the underside of the base of the penis, to its ultimate perceptible "roots" within the scrotum where he applies pressure and holds the imagery as he says one mantra.

His hands relax on the genitals.

His fingers slide around either side of the testicles and the tips rest on the perineum; pressure is applied; the image held; the mantra said twice.

His hands relax on his genitals.

His fingers slide downward, across the perineum, to the muscles at the entrance of the rectum; inward pressure is applied, the imagery held, the mantra said twice.

His hands relax on his genitals.

His hands slide upward to the base of the penis; fingers and thumbs encircle the penis; pressure is applied while two mantras are said and the imagery is held.

At the end of the mantras, the encircling pressure on the penis is maintained and the thumbs and fingers encircling the penis are drawn upward, along the shaft of the penis, over the glans, and away.

Then, immediately, the fingers and thumbs return to the base of the penis, encircle it again, squeeze, and slide along the shaft to the tip and away.

This action is repeated until a full, firm erection is attained.

Once the erection is attained, the Male begins masturbating, as he does alone in the Control Ritual.

He will, of course, be aware of the Female watching him. That is all the more reason he must maintain his imagery and attempt to masturbate as he would normally, if the Female were not there. He *must* maintain his position on the bed, eyes closed, using the imagery and the mantra.

The Female, without moving, should observe closely the movements of the Male's hands as he masturbates himself.

The Male *must* put total concentration into his actions and not be distracted by the Female's presence. He should be neither self-conscious nor out of Control because she is there. It is, after all, the purpose of the exercise to remove yet another remnant of self-conscious inhibition, and establish further the powers of Control.

The Male continues to masturbate until he feels orgasm approaching, at which point he should immediately cease to masturbate, return his hands to his abdomen, and repeat the Control Mantra, with the Control Yantra imagery of the "written words," until he has attained Control.

The Male will strongly desire to reach out for the Female and enter into sexual relations. And the ritual may have the same effect on the Female, who will wish to satisfy herself and the male because of the stimulation that has aroused them both.

But *Control* is the Key!

And Control must be attained and maintained. The Male must back away, under Control, from the verge of his orgasm. He must call on the Control Mantra and Yantra imagery, and use them with all his concentrative force.

As soon as Control is felt, the Male should switch from the Control Mantra to the Channeling Mantra and Yantra imagery, and make full use of this supercharged power to Channel the energy to other concerns.

Interspersed with the Channeling Mantra and Imagery, he may also repeat the Control Mantra and Imagery, to help him maintain control.

Once he feels that he *is* in complete Control, he may open his eyes and sit up. He must avoid touching the Female or himself, as he stands and steps away from the bed.

The Male and Female do not speak at this time.

When the Male steps away from the bed, the Female slowly stands and walks to the side of the bed then lies upon it in the prescribed position for her Awareness Rituals.

She closes her eyes and brings to mind the same Yantra imagery as when she performs this ritual alone. She must use great concentrative effort to fix and sustain the imagery, to avoid being distracted by the male's presence.

The Male sits quietly and passively on the foot of the bed. Though he has Control of himself, he has developed a powerful energy buildup by carrying himself to the verge of orgasm. For this reason, his observation of the Female during this ritual will be extremely stimulating, and while watching he may have to close his eyes on occasion and bring forth the Control Yantra imagery and say the Control Mantra (to himself) to avoid losing Control. Whatever he has to do, must be done quietly without moving. He must, under no circumstances, touch the Female or himself during the course of the ritual.

In her position on the bed, the Female fixes the Yantra imagery strongly in her mind, says the Awareness Mantra, then proceeds with Awareness Ritual and then the Control Ritual with modifications as follows:

She brings her hands from her abdomen to her lips, touches them lightly, says the mantra once, holds the yantra, and returns her hands to her abdomen.

She next brings her hands to her breasts; her fingers slide over each breast, to grasp the nipples and roll them gently, feeling the warm sensation while saying the mantra twice and holding the yantra. She returns her hands to her abdomen.

Then her hands slide slowly down the abdomen, through the pubic hair, across the mons veneris, to rest on either side of the vaginal opening. Her thumbs open the labia of the vagina and the index fingers press on the clitoris while two mantras are said.

She relaxes her hands and allows the vaginal labia to close.

She moves her hands downward until the fingertips rest on the perineum. Her fingers press on the perineum as she says the mantra twice.

Again her hands relax on the vagina.

The hands move downward, across the perineum, to the muscles at the entrance to the rectum. Her fingers apply inward pressure on the rectal opening. The mantra is said twice.

She returns her hands to the vagina and her thumbs open the labia as far as possible while her fingers press on the clitoris.

Then with fingers and thumbs, she begins masturbating, as she does when she practices the Control Ritual alone.

The Female will, of course, be aware that the Male is watching her, and she must attempt to masturbate as she would normally. She must maintain the position on the bed, eyes closed, using the imagery and the mantra.

The Male, without moving, should observe closely the movements of the Female's hands as she masturbates herself. He need not concern himself with her fantasy images, only with the way she touches and massages herself to bring her closer and closer to orgasm.

The Female should be neither self-conscious nor out of Control because the Male is present. She should continue to masturbate until she feels orgasm approaching. Then she should immediately cease masturbating, and switch from the yantra of masturbation and the Awareness Mantra, to the imagery of Control, saying and "writing" the Control Mantra on the black void of her Yantra.

Her hands should immediately return to their previous position, folded across her abdomen.

She may now have a very strong desire to reach out for the Male, draw him close, and make love. And the Male may be feeling the same desire.

But remember: *Control* is the Key!

And control must be attained and maintained by the Female now, as it was by the Male earlier. The Female must pull herself away from the impending orgasm, using all the concentrative efforts of the yantra and mantra to bring about that Control.

Once the Female has attained Control, she should switch from the Control Mantra and Yantra to the yantra and mantra of Channeling, making use of the great power that she has generated. She may alternate between the Control Mantra and Yantra imagery, and the Channeling Mantra and Yantra imagery, using each in turn, maintaining Control and utilizing that Control and energy to the fullest.

Once the Female feels she has complete Control, and she has finished her Channeling, she may open her eyes and sit up on the edge of the bed.

When she and the Male look at each other, in this highly charged state, they must continue to exercise their Controls, to overcome any desire to touch, stimulate, or do anything else that might lead to sexual foreplay and lovemaking.

You must not touch. You must not speak.

Walk silently from the room to your table, and sit. Use the yantra and mantra of Control and the yantra and mantra of Channeling, as needed and desired.

Pour the wine and begin the repast.

As you drink and eat, relax, but always remain in Control.

The One-Hour Rule, in full, is to be observed this night.

Now you should talk. Exchange frank and honest feelings and ideas on what you have just witnessed and felt. But maintain Control. If, in the middle of a sentence, you feel the resurgence of stimulation and desire, use the Control Mantra and Yantra imagery. When one of you sees the other suddenly close her or his eyes tight, you should be aware that Control is being called forth; and silence should prevail as long as either partner is seeking Control.

This should be part of the Tantric bond between you —that you recognize the tightly closed eyes as a signal that one of you is calling forth mantras and yantra imagery. And the response should be a respectful silence.

The purposes of this ritual are obvious:

1. To remove self-consciousness. The act of masturbation is usually a solitary one. By allowing your partner to witness this very private practice, you have removed another vestige of modesty and self-consciousness.

2. Removal of inhibition. It may have proven difficult to go through the process of masturbation while being watched, particularly if your partner has never observed you before. By going through the act, to the verge of orgasm, you have removed an inhibiting influence within you. That is why there must never be any faking of impending orgasm. It must be carried out "for real" or you defeat the Tantric purpose.

3. Control. Control on the part of both partners; Control through concentrative yantra imagery, though your partner is present and watching; Control of the orgasm, under these difficult circumstances; Control, to prevent either of you from engaging the other in sexual relations, even under the highly stimulating conditions.

4. Awareness. A different Awareness: An Awareness of how your partner, in the private moments of masturbation, prefers to be stimulated; how he or she handles and fondles and massages and stim-

ulates himself or herself. With this knowledge, you are able to be a better love and sex partner to each other.

You should openly discuss these four aspects of this ritual. Honesty and candor in discussing the exercise itself, and the purpose outlined, will lead to a greater mental and emotional awareness of what you now know physically. This is the doorway through which Tantric Sex would take all couples—opening the way to communication about all facets of sex; leading the way to communication about the accompanying emotions; guiding the way to greater mental and spiritual understanding between the partners, even to coordination of Channeling efforts. Your sexual relations will reach new levels of ecstasy and union.

The bond created by the Tantra is a special bond. It exists within the Tantriks themselves and is hardly expected to be understood or appreciated by those who have never experienced the sharing and openness of the ways of the Tantra, or the Controls that make it possible.

At the end of their hour, the couple may release their Controls to whatever degree they wish, and go to bed to make love.

And, as on each night, call forth the Channeling Yantra and Mantra as you relax your bodies and minds and drift into sleep.

Channeling can make awaking each morning as brightly stimulating as the lovemaking of the night before.

THE FIFTH NIGHT OF THE TANTRA

The Initiates asked of the Tantric Master:
  "Is not the goal you set for us beyond our grasp?"
  And the Tantric Master replied:
  "As you became aware of your Tantric being through the Rituals you have performed alone, so you can become aware of the being of the Tantrik who shares your pleasure.

  "And as you have sought to master your body's pleasure through Rituals, you now become the instrument by which the Tantrik who shares your awareness and pleasure shall increase pleasure and master it.

  "Were the goal easily grasped, it would be of no value. It is the mastery of pleasure that shall multiply your pleasure.

  "It is the multiplying of pleasure, and the mastery of its new heights, that shall mark each step along the climb upward to total mastery of life and the universe."

The climb becomes more precipitous with this ritual.

The setting is the same as for the previous rituals for couples. You sit at the table and discuss and think about this ritual and the subject of your Channeling.

When your glasses of wine have been drunk, the Female stands, says, "I am ready," and slowly removes her clothes as the Male watches. Then she sits and the Male stands, says, "I am ready," and slowly removes his clothes.

Totally nude, you kiss and embrace, then walk to the bath.

The now-regular procedure of the bath is to be followed.

Following the bath, you return to the table and sit silently for a few minutes.

Then pillows are moved away from the table, and you sit facing each other, in the Contemplative Position of Tantra, your hands on each others' knees.

You say three Awareness Mantras

The Male says, "I am ready"; the Female removes her hands from his knees, leans forward from the pelvis, to "cup" the Male's penis and testicles, as in previous practice of this ritual.

Once the Male's genitals are encircled and held, the Female says, "I am ready."

The Male then proceeds with the muscular contractions. After the third contraction, the Female slides her hands, still encircling the penis, away from the base of the penis, along the penis shaft, over the glans, releasing the penis and returning her hands to his knees.

Three Awareness Mantras are said.

The Female says, "I am ready," and the Male removes his right hand from her knee, leans forward from the pelvis, and inserts his index finger in her vagina.

The Male says, "I am ready."

The Female proceeds with her muscular contractions, contracting the muscles three times, following the same procedure and wording as on the previous nights.

After the third contraction, the Male removes his finger from the vagina, with a slight pressure, tracing the finger across the urethral opening and clitoris, then away from the vagina and back to her knee.

Now sit silently for a few moments in the Contemplative Position. Then rise, embrace, kiss, and walk together to the bedroom.

The Female lies on her back on the bed in the Awareness position, knees apart, bottoms of feet touching, hands folded across the abdomen.

The Male sits on the bed *beside* her, right on the edge of the bed, his buttocks approximately alongside her stomach. He should keep his feet on the floor, or dangling over the side of the bed, and sit upright. His body should *not* be in contact with hers. He sits facing the head of the bed, looking down on her breasts and face, his hands on his lap.

The Female now closes her eyes tightly. She says three Awareness Mantras, then says aloud, "I am ready." She now fixes all her concentration on the yantra imagery of Awareness.

In this ritual, the Male and Female are to do *only* as they are directed. There should be no actions that are not specifically called for.

The Male proceeds as follows:

With his eyes open, he gazes down at the Female lying before him, her eyes closed tightly. He says the Awareness Mantra twice.

He then slowly lifts his hands and places the index fingers of both hands to her lips, running them along the outline of her lips, softly, as he says three mantras.

Then he returns his hands to his lap (resting on his legs or thighs, or wherever he chooses, so long as they do not contact the Female, nor touch his genitals).

Now the Male lifts his hands again and moves them to the Female's breasts, letting them relax, covering each breast with the palm of one hand. Then he slides his hands down along the breasts until the index finger and thumb of each hand reach the nipples. He gently rolls the nipples between his index fingers and thumbs while saying three mantras. Then he returns his hands to the relaxed position on his lap.

At this point, the Male quietly swings around on the bed, still staying on the Female's right, his legs still off the bed. He is now facing the foot of the bed, looking down on the Female's legs, pubis, and abdomen.

The Female maintains her position, without moving. She says the mantras as he touches each part of her body, and she holds the image of herself on the bed, each part of her body in turn being touched by the Male.

The Male now places his hands on top of the Female's hands, which are resting on her abdomen. Then he slides his hands downward on the abdomen, through the pubic hair, across the mons veneris, to rest on either side of the vagina, as he saw the Female do in her Awareness and Control Rituals.

Then the Male's thumbs part the labia of the vagina and his index fingers press on the clitoris, stroking it gently as he says two Mantras. Then he removes his fingers from the clitoris, allows the labia to close, and lets his hands lie, without pressure, on top of the vagina.

The Male says two Awareness Mantras. Then he slides his fingers lightly along the labia of the vagina, downward to the perineum, where he presses with the tips of his index fingers while saying two mantras.

Once again he allows his hands to relax.

After saying two mantras, he uses his thumbs to part the labia. His fingers again press on the clitoris.

He now continues to press on the clitoris and says these words: "I feel."

When he says these words, the Female responds, "I feel," *if* the pressure he is exerting is precisely on the clitoris. If, for some reason it is not exactly where she wishes it to be on the clitoris, she should reach down to adjust the Male's fingers to the precise spot where she desires his finger to press on the clitoris. Once the pressure is where she wishes it, she takes away her hands and says, "I feel."

The Male should note, by feel and by looking closely (mostly by feel), precisely where the pressure is desired. This is important.

Once the Female has returned her hands to her abdomen or said "I feel," the Male should relax his hands, remove his finger from the clitoris, allow the labia to close, and rest his hands on her vagina.

He says two mantras.

Then he slides his hands downward again along the labia, across the perineum until his fingertips touch the muscles of the rectal opening, where he presses and says three mantras.

Once again he relaxes his hands, allowing them to lie quietly atop the vagina while he says the mantras twice.

Then the Male uses his thumbs to open the labia and press with his fingertips on the clitoris. He says the mantra twice, slides the index finger of his left hand into the vagina a short distance, while his right index finger and thumb begin to massage the clitoris and he begins to masturbate the female, trying to duplicate, as near as possible, the actions he has witnessed when she masturbated herself.

The Male must *not* enter into any other actions except the act of masturbating the Female. No part of his body should touch hers except the hands he is using to stimulate her. The Female must hold onto the imagery she has of herself being masturbated by the Male. She says the Awareness Mantra over and over as her stimulation intensifies.

The Female must *not* move her hands from her abdomen until she feels the approach of her orgasm. When the orgasm begins to mount and is impending, as when she is masturbating herself, she takes her right hand from her abdomen, grasps the Male's arm or shoulder, and begins to use the Control Mantra, along with the Control Yantra imagery.

When she grasps the Male's arm or shoulder, it should be with force, pressing her fingers into his flesh, to signal him that she is switching to the Control Mantra and Yantra imagery.

The Male should remove his hands from the Female's vagina *immediately* when she reaches out and grasps him.

This signal will be used in many other areas of the Tantra. And, as a signal, it *must* be acknowledged and obeyed by the recipient.

In this case, the Male is not to add even one additional stroke, touch, or movement once the Female has given him the signal.

He ceases touching her, completely.

And since, at this point, the Male has been touching the vagina and watching the stimulation of the Female, he will also find himself in a very sexually excited condition. He, too, should start saying the Control Mantra and using the Control Yantra imagery.

This is one of the most difficult points of Control in the Tantric exercises. The Male and Female are in the throes of intense sexual stimulation, and there may be almost overpowering desires to deviate from the exercise and engage in sexual foreplay and intercourse.

This must *not* occur!

It is the *Control* that will eventually bring a hundred times the pleasures. But the Control must be attained and maintained. Without the Control there is no Tantra. The goals are worthless if the Controls are not learned and made a part of the ritual.

It may take time to master the Control. In fact, you may even lose Control in the highly stimulated atmosphere of the rituals. If so, you cease the ritual and try it again, from the beginning, after a few hours—or repeat it the following night.

Do not become discouraged. Control is attainable, and if the rituals are followed in a slow, deliberate manner, Control can be reached and maintained.

The Female, using her Control Mantra and Yantra imagery, will slowly bring herself back from the impending orgasm to the point of complete Control, and will then alternate between the Control Yantra and Mantra and the Channeling Yantra and Mantra, which will help reinforce the Control and at the same time put the powerful energy forces of her state of stimulation to use in other areas.

When the Female starts with the Control Mantra and Yantra, the Male should rise and stand several feet away from the bed, in order to watch the Female attain her control, and at the same time achieve his own Control, to prevent his touching or otherwise further stimulating the Female or himself.

Once the Female has attained control and maintained it while using the Channeling Mantra and Yantra, she should try to relax on the bed. Then she opens her eyes, sits up, and rises from the bed. She must avoid touching the Male.

They are to remain silent.

Now it is the Male's turn to lie on the bed, on his back, knees apart, soles of feet touching; eyes closed. He says the Awareness Mantra three times and establishes the imagery of himself on the bed, the Female seated beside him.

The Female sits on his right side on the edge of the bed, her feet hanging off the bed or resting on the floor, her hands folded on her lap facing the head of the bed, looking down at the Male's face and chest.

No part of the Female's body may touch the Male's.

Because the Male has been stimulated masturbating the Female, his Control may be under great pressure at this time.

Once the Male has established his imagery, he says, "I am ready."

The Female then raises her hands and touches her fingertips to the Male's lips, running her fingers along the outline of his lips and saying two mantras.

Then she returns her hands to the relaxed position on her lap and says two mantras.

Her hands next move to the Male's breasts and lie palm down on them. Then the thumb and index fingers of each hand take the nipples and roll them gently while saying two mantras.

The Female's hands return to the relaxed position on her lap.

The Female now swerves her body around, without moving her buttocks off the bed, her feet still off the bed, so that now she is facing the foot of the bed, looking down at the Male's legs, abdomen, and genitals.

She places her hands, palms down, on top of the Male's hands folded across his abdomen.

Then she moves her hands from atop the Male's, and slides her fingers downward on his abdomen, through the pubic hair, and encircles his penis with forefingers and thumbs, applying squeezing pressure. She says three mantras; then—continuing to hold the penis at its base—she slides her fingers away from his body, up the shaft of the penis to the glans. If the Male has a firm erection, she takes the tip of the penis between thumbs and forefingers and slowly squeezes it, watching as it actually diminishes slightly in size, as if the "air" were being squeezed from it. This action will actually lessen the sensitivity of the glans and hence of the penis, and make control easier for the male. Then she releases the penis.

The Female allows her hands to relax on either side of the Male organs, as she says two Mantras.

Her fingers slide downward, tracing the underside of the penis to its perceptible "base" within the scrotum. She maintains the pressure there through two Mantras, then releases the pressure and lets her hands relax on either side of the penis and testicles.

Now her fingers slide downward, around the testicles, under them, to press on the perineum. The pressure is maintained through two mantras, then the hands relax, but stay where they are while two more mantras are said.

She again slides her hands downward, until her fingertips touch the muscles at the rectal opening. The fingers press inward on the rectal muscles while three mantras are said. Then the hands slide back up to relax on either side of the penis.

Three mantras are now said.

Then the thumbs and index fingers encircle the penis and slide upward along its shaft.

At this point the Female begins the process of masturbating the Male, emulating as nearly as possible the motions she witnessed him using when he masturbated himself.

The Female should not become alarmed if she notices a bead of semen forming at the opening at the head of the penis. This is normal for males in a high state of sexual excitement and does *not* mean that the Male is about to have an orgasm and ejaculate. This bead of semen may in fact be used to rub up and down the shaft of the penis, as a sort of natural lubricant in masturbation.

Because the Male entered into this exercise already in a highly stimulated condition, it may not take long for him to come close to orgasm.

As soon as the Male feels the first approach of orgasm, he should signal the Female by removing his right hand from his abdomen and reaching out and grasping her shoulder and arm, with sufficient force so that she is aware that this is the signal.

The very instant that the Female receives this signal, she must immediately cease all movement and remove her hands completely from the Male.

Here it must be emphasized again that the Male must pull for complete Control, including overcoming any desire to have the Female masturbate him to orgasm. Otherwise, the entire purpose of the Tantric exercises will be lost.

When the Male senses the approach of orgasm, as when he masturbates himself, he must immediately signal the Female, and allow her to move away from him.

He must, at once, start using the Control Yantra imagery and the Control Mantra, to bring the needed Control.

The Female should rise from the bed and stand a few feet away, to wait silently and watch while the Male attains his Control.

The Male should alternate between the Control Yantra and Mantra and the Channeling Yantra and Mantra, until absolute Control has been attained and maintained.

Only then may he open his eyes and get up from the bed.

He must avoid touching the Female, and she him.

Now walk from the bedroom, back to the low table. Silently sip your wine and eat your food. You may call upon your Control Yantra and Mantra, as needed. Each of you will respect the other's control and will be silent at all times when the partner squeezes eyes closed and is obviously striving for additional Control or Channeling.

You should now talk about the ritual and exchange thoughts and feelings, as you eat.

At the end of the hour, you will know that you have accomplished one of the most difficult exercises of the Tantra. And you may now enter into lovemaking in any way you wish. The extremely charged stimulation of masturbating your partner to the point of unfulfilled orgasm, and in turn being masturbated to the verge of orgasm, will bring incredibly heightened pleasure to your lovemaking.

You will be more aware than ever of your own sexual sensitivity, and that of your partner. You will be able to bring your partner to new heights of sexual ecstasy. And the Control you have exercised will result in orgasms of greater power and duration than any you have ever known.

Once your highly acute sexual stimulation has been satisfied and you are ready for sleep, the Tantra reminds you that every night, for the rest of your lives, you should fall asleep utilizing the Channeling Mantra and Yantra imagery, to help your life be more what you want it to be, through the use of the same great energy source that has brought you the pleasure of this night.

THE SIXTH NIGHT OF THE TANTRA

The Couple stood before the Tantric Master, who spoke to them:

"You have traveled far on the climb upward. Your initiation nears its end. Yet questions remain. Questions which you shall answer yourselves, through giving to each other.

"As you embark this night, you shall each explore the other in still another way, to gain Tantric knowledge each of the other. You shall not refrain or withdraw. The ritual shall bring new delights. And in its pleasures you shall know greater mastery over self and others.

"Your body is as the instrument of the master musician. It is to be played in all possible combinations. Only in this way will you explore the passageways to creative mastery."

As on previous nights, sit together at the table and slowly sip one glass of wine each while thinking of the Ritual and the Channeling you wish to accomplish.

When your glass of wine has been drunk, the Male stands, says, "I am ready," and removes his clothes. Then he sits.

The Female stands, says, "I am ready," and removes her clothes. The ritual should be followed as it has on all previous nights.

Now walk to the bath and proceed with the Bath Ritual.

Afterward return to the low table, sit silently for a

few minutes, repeating the Awareness Mantra in preparation for the ritual.

Then move the pillows from the low table and sit facing each other in the Contemplative Position of Tantra.

Now the rituals using the muscular contractions are followed completely, in every detail, as they have been on previous nights.

Once this is completed, continue to sit quietly in the Contemplative Position for a few minutes. Then stand, embrace and kiss.

Walk together to the bedroom.

The Female lies on her back on the bed in the Awareness Position. The Male sits on the edge of the bed, to the Female's right. His buttocks should be about at the Female's waist, his legs hanging off the side of the bed; he is facing the head of the bed, looking down on her head and breasts.

The Female closes her eyes tightly, calls forth the yantra imagery of herself, says the Awareness Mantra three times, and then says, "I am ready." She now lies still and waits.

With his eyes open, the Male says the Awareness Mantra twice to himself, then lifts his hands and places the index fingers to her lips, tracing the outline of the lips; then he cups her face in the palm of his hand, and trying not to touch any other part of her body, he leans over and touches his lips gently to her lips, slowly running the tip of his tongue along the outline of her lips, then kissing her strongly, while he says the Awareness Mantra three times to himself. Then, exercising Control, he removes his lips from hers and sits, hands on lap.

The Female is not to respond to the kiss, except to

part her lips in reaction to the Male's kiss. She is to concentrate on the feel of his lips and tongue, and is not to make any overt action of response.

The Male says the Awareness Mantra twice, then he places his hands on the Female's breasts, palms down, then he takes each nipple between index finger and thumb, and rolls the nipple gently. Once this is done, the Male removes his left hand from her right breast. He keeps his right hand on her left breast and massages it gently as he leans over and takes the nipple into his mouth, gently sucking it while he runs the tip of his tongue around the nipple while saying three mantras. Then he removes his mouth from her breast and sits upright.

He also removes his right hand from her left breast, and places his left hand on her right breast, massaging it gently and leaning forward to take the right nipple in his mouth, sucking gently and running the tip of his tongue around the nipple saying three mantras. Then he removes his mouth from her breast and sits upright.

Now quietly the Male swings around to face the foot of the bed and look down on the Female's legs, genitals, and abdomen.

He lays his hands atop the Female's hands on her abdomen, then slides them downward through the pubic hair, across the mons veneris, allowing them to lie on either side of the vaginal opening.

He opens the labia with his thumbs and presses on the clitoris while saying the mantra three times.

Then he slides his hands downward until his fingertips press on the perineum, as he says the mantra three times.

He relaxes his hands atop the vagina.

He slides his hands downward so that the fingertips move across the perineum and touch the rectal muscles, exerting inward pressure and saying the mantra three times.

His thumbs open the labia and his fingertips exert Awareness pressure on the clitoris, while he repeats the mantra three times.

Then he allows the labia to close, his hands remaining on the vagina.

He leans forward and brings his head to the vaginal area.

His lips touch and kiss the inside of the thighs, first left, then right, his tongue tracing a path from inside the thigh downward to the side of the vagina.

Using the thumb and forefinger of his right hand, he parts the labia. His lips touch and, with a slight sucking motion, pulls into his mouth the labia of one side of the vagina; the tongue moving back and forth on the labia as the suction is maintained. Then he releases that labia and repeats the action on the labia on the other side of the vaginal opening.

Then his tongue traces the outline of the vaginal orifice, all the way round, and then enters the vaginal opening, to move up and down on the upper vaginal walls near the opening. The vagina is, of course, "upside down" to the Male. As he runs his tongue downward, into the vagina, he will feel the indentation of the urethral opening and stimulate it; then he will slide his tongue back upward, toward the clitoris, which he will stimulate slowly with his tongue. Then, his lips encircling the clitoris, he will create a slight suction and draw the clitoris between his lips and begin to stimulate it with his tongue.

At this point the Female may move her hips and body in response to the Male, in whatever manner she pleases, though she should maintain the basic position, knees apart, feet together.

The Male should remain totally aware of the Female's responses and, when a response is strong, repeat the stimulation which created that response.

The Male, may, once the Female is responding strongly, insert his right thumb into her vagina, allowing it to rest within the vagina, without moving the thumb itself, to create additional stimulation. He continues oral stimulation, sucking, probing, kissing, licking—to bring the Female toward orgasm.

The Male must not touch any other part of the Female's body.

The Female must keep her hands crossed on her abdomen. She must not reach out for the Male or touch his body.

When the Female feels orgasm approaching, she removes her hand from her abdomen and grasps the Male's arm or shoulder to signal him.

When he feels her grasp, the Male responds immediately by removing his mouth and hands from her vagina and sits upright. He then stands and moves away from the bed.

The Female will immediately switch to Control Yantra imagery and the Control Mantra, and then, upon attaining Control, switch to the Channeling Yantra Imagery and Mantra.

She will return her hands to her abdomen, retain the position and now, through solitary effort, pull for the Control that is so vital.

The Male must remain silent, watching, and using the Control Mantra and Control Imagery to maintain his Control.

This is yet another phase of Tantric Control, and difficult as it may be, both partners must attain and maintain complete Control. Only through such Control can the total concept of Tantra be learned and put to work for you.

By now the Couple has already learned that the preceding exercises have begun to make a difference in their sexual and emotional relationship, and that the Channeling has begun to make a difference in their lives.

With each new conquest of Control, the subsequent values of that Control become more and more evident.

Once she has attained Control, and has utilized the Channeling, the Female may open her eyes and sit up.

She should then rise from the bed and stand.

There must be no contact between the Female and Male at this point—not a word, nor a touch.

They should stand apart for a few minutes, continuing to reinforce the Control they have attained.

The Male may, at this point wish to use the Control Yantra imagery as he lies down on the bed, for he has been highly stimulated by orally stimulating the Female and by her responses, as well as by the anticipation of the ritual.

He should lie on his back, knees apart, feet pressed together, in the Awareness Position. He should pull for Control and the Female should not sit on the bed beside him until he has attained complete, relaxed Control and says, "I am ready."

When he says this, the Female should sit on the edge of the bed, on the right of the Male, her feet off the bed, careful not to touch him except as directed.

The Female, eyes open, faces the head of the bed, looking down on the Male's face and chest. His eyes are closed tight.

The Female raises her hands and moves her index fingers and thumbs to the Male's lips, running them along the outline of his lips, while saying three times the mantra of Awareness.

Then her hands cup his face and she leans forward, to place her lips gently against his. Slowly she runs the tip of her tongue along his lips, back and forth, while saying three mantras to herself. Then she presses her lips against his and probes his mouth with her tongue while saying three mantras.

During this kiss, the Male should remain passive, concentrating on the imagery of what is being done and the feelings created.

Then the Female pulls her mouth away from the Male and sits up.

She says the Awareness Mantra three times.

Then she places her hands, palms down, on each of the Male's breasts. Slowly she slides her hands to grasp the nipple of each breast between a thumb and index finger and rolls it gently. Then while her right hand remains on his left breast she removes her left hand from his right breast.

With her right hand, she massages the left breast, then leans over and sucks the nipple into her mouth, running her tongue back and forth over the nipple while saying three mantras to herself.

Then she removes her mouth and her right hand from his left breast and sits up.

She now places her left hand on his right breast, leans forward, and sucks the nipple into her mouth and runs her tongue back and forth over the nipple while saying three mantras.

Then she removes her lips and left hand from his right breast.

She turns quietly on the bed, so that she is facing the foot of the bed, looking down on the Male's abdomen, genitals, and legs.

She says the mantra twice.

She lays the palms of her hands on his abdomen, then slides them down through the pubic hair to the base of the penis, which she encircles with her thumbs and index fingers. She squeezes, while saying three Mantras, then slides her fingers and thumbs, still squeezing the penis, from the base upward away from his body, along the shaft of the penis, to the glans, holding the glans between fingers and thumbs and "squeezing" it so that its size becomes perceptibly smaller; then pulling her hands away from the penis, to rest on either side of the genitals.

She says two mantras.

Her fingers trace the underside of the penis down into the scrotum, to the very base, where she applies pressure while saying three mantras.

The fingers now trace downward again, around the testicles to touch the perineum; the fingertips applying awareness pressure to the perineum while three mantras are said.

Then the hands are relaxed again and two mantras said.

She slides her hands downward, across the perineum until the tips press on the muscles at the rectal entrance, she repeats three mantras, then relaxes her hands.

Now the Female returns her hands to rest on the sides of the genitals.

She says two mantras.

Her index fingers and thumbs encircle the base of the penis and squeeze as she leans forward until her head reaches the penis.

At this point, she removes her *left* index finger and thumb from the base of the penis and with her left hand she cups the testicles.

Her right index finger and thumb continue to encircle the base of the penis in a tight grip.

She now uses her right index finger and thumb to press the erect penis "upward" until the glans touches the Male's abdomen. She then places her lips against the outline of the tube-like urethral outline on the underside of the penis, at the base. Covering her teeth with her lips, she presses her lips against the urethral outline and slides her lips slowly along the outline, toward the glans.

When her lips reach the glans, she lifts her mouth away and using her right hand, holds the penis at an erect, natural angle, perpendicular to the Male's body.

She takes the glans portion of the penis into her mouth. Her lips are comfortably curved inward over her teeth. She encompasses only the head of the penis in her mouth. She sucks and at the same time runs her tongue around the glans.

Then slowly she allows the entire penis to slide into her mouth, taking as much of it as she comfortably can. While sucking, she slides her head away from the base, to the glans; then downward again, toward the base.

Her left hand is massaging the Male's testicles, perineum, and rectal muscles. Her right hand should not leave its "grip" encircling the base of the penis.

Now her movements will be guided by the Male's response. When he reacts strongly to a given action, the Female should repeat the action and bring him closer and closer to orgasm.

The Male is to lie passive. He is not to touch the Female in any way. Nor is he to allow Control to get away from him. He must, at the first sign of impending orgasm, lift his right hand from his abdomen and grasp the Female's arm or shoulder, to signal her.

Once the signal is received, the Female should remove her mouth and her hands from the Male's penis and testicles. She should sit up, get up from the bed, and stand several feet away, silently.

The Male must give the signal in time to prevent the orgasm. He should have mastered this in previous exercises, and that mastery will now prove its worth as he struggles for control under these very difficult circumstances.

The Male, when he gives the signal, should switch at once to Control Yantra imagery and the Control Mantra. He should use these until he feels that control has been attained and can be maintained. Then he uses the Channeling Yantra Imagery and Mantra to direct the great store of concentrative energy that has been amassed.

Once he has attained Control and maintained it, then uses that Channeling Yantra and Mantra, he may open his eyes and sit up. Then he should stand, and say nothing.

The Couple should silently walk from the bedroom to the table and pour a glass of wine. As on previous nights, enter freely into a discussion of the ritual with the understanding that you will respect each other's need for control. And each of you will use the mantra and yantra of Control as often as necessary to maintain control during the next hour—for the One-Hour Rule is in effect.

The Tantric use of cunnilingus and fellatio serves a dual purpose which should be clear:

The intimacy of such acts brings about a more total understanding of the partner, and the acts themselves provide a basis for further removal of all inhibitions between the partners.

If fellatio and cunnilingus have been a part of your

sexual relationship before, then the intimacy, stimulation, and desire to please are reinforced through the
deliberate ritualistic approach provided in this Tantric
Ritual.

If you have not engaged in oral sex before, then an
entire new area of intimacy, without inhibition and
self-consciousness, is entered.

To all couples the Tantric approach brings new
awareness and increased pleasure. And Control plays a
great part in this, as always.

Through these rituals, you learn the extent not only
of your own Control but also of the Control that your
partner is capable of maintaining. This sharing in each
other's Control capabilities brings about a deeper feeling of trust. When your partner says, "I will control,"
you know that he or she does have the ability to do as
promised.

You should enjoy the repast and discuss whatever
you wish, while maintaining Control during the hour.

Then you may retire, to seek whatever pleasures you
will. If oral lovemaking has not been a part of foreplay
or satisfaction in your relationship before, it now will
be. If it has been a part before, the Tantric approach
should heighten its meaning and pleasure.

And, eventually, there will come sleep. And with
each night's sleep, whether there has been lovemaking
or not, the Channeling Yantra and Mantra should be, by
now, as much a part of the process as closing your eyes;
a natural, easy prelude to sleep. And one that will make
each day of the Tantra, and of the rest of your life, better than the one before.

THE SEVENTH NIGHT OF THE TANTRA

The Tantric Master spoke:

"The joys of Kali and Mahakala are yours. You share the pleasures. You speak of the pleasures. You each know your pleasure, and the pleasure of the other.

"Move together yet separately into this night and all nights of your life. Draw ever new pleasure. Give ever increasing pleasure.

"Create greater energy to master. Create the Tantric Life from your own being."

The instructions for this ritual should be read in conjunction with the "Continuation" chapter, which immediately follows.

The setting is the same as on the previous nights; the low table laid out with food and wine; the couple seated, drinking their first glass of wine together.

The Male then stands, says, "I am ready," and slowly removes all of his clothes, then sits again.

The Female stands and says, "I am ready," and removes all of her clothes, then sits.

After a few moments' silence, they stand, embrace, and kiss. Then they walk to the bath.

The Bath Ritual is followed as on all other nights.

Then they return to the table, move their pillows away from it, and assume the Contemplative Position of Tantra. As previously done, they now enter into the Ritual.

When the muscular contractions are completed, they remain in the Contemplative Position for a few minutes before rising. Then they walk to the bedroom.

The Female lies on her back on the bed in the Awareness Position, knees apart, soles of feet pressed together.

The Male sits on the bed beside her.

The Male keeps his eyes open. The Female keeps her eyes *open*.

Now the Male will go through the ritual, as directed. As he proceeds, the Female must tell him openly and honestly the feelings of stimulation and arousal that each of his actions is creating within her. The Male will not only become more familiar visually with each area of her body, but will also have a more definite knowledge of which of his actions is most pleasing and stimulating.

The Male touches the Female's lips and she tells him her feelings.

The Male kisses the Female's lips, and she tells him (after the kiss) what her feelings were.

They each now say the Awareness Mantra twice.

The Male touches and massages the Female's breasts; then rolls the nipples between index fingers and thumbs; then kisses the breasts. The Female describes her sensations, telling the Male explicitly how she feels as he does this.

The Male now turns on the bed, facing the feet.

He runs his fingertips and thumbs along the abdomen, to the vagina; opening the labia; applying pressure to the clitoris. Then he relaxes and the Female describes her feelings.

Now the Male runs his fingertips to the perineum, presses, then relaxes. The Female describes the sensation to him.

The Male slides his fingertips downward and touches the rectal muscles, exerts pressure, then relaxes, and the Female describes her sensations.

Then the Male moves his hands back to the vagina, parts the labia and begins a slow prelude to masturbation, pausing as he stimulates each area, or alters his actions, and the Female relates her reaction to each movement and point of stimulation.

The Male now bends forward and begins to orally stimulate the vaginal area, the labia, the vagina, and the clitoris. As he kisses each area, the Female describes her sensations.

It is *not* the purpose to stimulate the Female to the point of orgasm. These described actions are intended to give the Male a deeper understanding of the Female's body and a deeper awareness of her responses.

The Female is to concentrate on each action by the Male and attempt to verbalize as accurately as possible what she is feeling; whether one action is more or less stimulating than another, etc.

The Male should then stop his actions after only a few minutes. He must not, at this point, attempt to stimulate the Female more than nominally.

The Male stands.

The Female sits up, then stands.

The Male assumes the Awareness position on the bed.

The Female sits beside him, facing the head of the bed.

The Male lies passively and, as the Female performs the prescribed actions, the Male describes the sensations he is feeling.

The Female touches the Male's lips, then she kisses his lips.

She then relaxes.

She leans over and massages his breasts, then rolls the nipples between index fingers and thumbs, then kisses the breasts. The Male tells her how this feels to him.

The Female now turns around to face the foot of the bed.

She slides her hands down his abdomen and encircles the base of the penis, squeezing. The Male describes his feelings, in detail.

Now, as she does each of the following, the Female will pause afterward, relax her hands, and wait for the Male's description of the sensation she has created by her actions.

The Female draws her encircling fingers along the shaft of the penis, still maintaining the squeezing pressure, and pauses at the glans.

She squeezes the glans itself then relaxes her hands on either side of the penis.

Her fingers trace the underside of the penis downward to its base within the scrotum. Then relax.

Her fingers slide downward to the perineum, exert pressure, and relax.

Her fingers slide downward farther to the rectal muscles, exert pressure, and relax.

After the Male has told her of the sensations at each point of pressure, the Female allows her hands to relax for a few moments before proceeding to the next.

Her right index finger and thumb now encircle and squeeze the base of the penis; her left hand "cups" the testicles.

The Female leans forward and begins orally stimulating the Male.

The Male describes the sensation of each movement.

Once the Female has gone through each of the phases of oral stimulation, she removes her mouth and hands from the Male's genitals and sits upright, apart from him.

The Male and Female *must* understand that this is a ritual based on increasing Awareness and communication. It is not intended to create stimulation, though the actions of the ritual itself are stimulating.

Calling for Control through the Control Mantra and Yantra imagery should not be necessary because the actions should be only cursory and not proceed sufficiently to bring about the approach of orgasm.

However, they should now both utilize the Control Mantra and Yantra as they sit apart for a few minutes. While using their Control, they should not converse.

The use of Control, now, before the next phase is vital. Both partners must be in Control for the remainder of the ritual.

The Male now lies upon the bed, on his back, in the Awareness position.

He closes his eyes tightly and says three Control Mantras, and brings forth the Control Yantra imagery, "writing" the words of the mantra on the void of his mind.

The Female stands and waits.

When he is sure within himself that he is in Control, the Male says, "I am ready."

The Female sits on the bed beside him and encircles the base of his penis with the index finger and thumb of her right hand. Maintaining squeezing pressure, she slides her fingers upward along the base of the penis, to the glans, across the glans, and releases the penis.

If the penis is stiffly erect, this act is done by the Female only *once*. Should the penis not be completely erect, she returns to encircle the base a second time, and repeat the action. The action, it must be reminded,

is only *from the base to the glans*—the encircling finger
and thumb toward the glans, over the glans, then releasing.

With the penis erect, the Female ceases the action.

She now says, "I am ready."

Then she straddles the Male's pelvis, facing his head.
Her straddling position should be "on her knees" with
her torso erect.

The Female now reaches down and again encircles the penis with her right index finger and thumb.
Her left hand is on her thigh or wherever it is comfortable and helps her maintain balance.

She raises her hips over the penis and guides it into
her vagina, then lowers herself onto it, until the penis
is comfortably in the vagina as deep as possible.

She sits very still. The Male remains still.

The Female places her hands on top of the Male's
hands, which are folded across his abdomen.

The Female closes her eyes tight.

The Male now focuses his imagery on the muscular
contractions. He concentrates on the muscles and
"tubes" within his penis, envisioning them filling as he
contracts the penile, groin, and abdominal muscles. He
holds the contraction for as long as he can, then relaxes
it.

The Female will feel the contraction-movement of
the penis within her vagina, and when it is relaxed, she
says, "I feel."

The Male now repeats the contraction, then relaxes
again, and the Female says, "I feel."

After a moment of concentration, the Male does the
contraction a third time, holding it for as long as is
possible, then relaxing. Once he has completed the
third contraction, the Female says, "I feel."

Then Male and Female sit silently, joined in this position for a few moments.

The Female, her eyes still tightly closed, now focuses her imagery on the vaginal muscles.

Once the Imagery and concentration are at the desired level, she contracts the vaginal muscles as tightly as possible, holding the contraction as long as she can, then relaxing.

The Male will feel the vaginal muscles contracting around his penis. When she relaxes the contraction, he will say, "I feel."

A second contraction is then done by the Female, after which she relaxes again and the Male says, "I feel."

Then the Female does a third contraction, as strongly as she possibly can, and holds it for as long as possible before relaxing.

When she does relax, the Male says, "I feel."

Now the Couple stays in this position quietly, exercising control while calling forth the Control Mantra and Imagery to help them maintain the Control.

The Male now relaxes his legs.

The Female begins to move her hips in whatever manner is pleasing to her and the Male. You begin to have intercourse in the Woman Above position. You may pursue your pleasure in this position by whatever movements of body, touching, and stimulating you desire—but you must maintain *Control!*

You must always remain aware that you both are seeking to keep your Control intact. Whenever one of you feels orgasm approaching, you must *signal* the other by grasping her or his arm or shoulder. At that point the action must stop, while Control is attained. This requires total cooperation from both partners, and respect for each other's desire for Control.

The Couple should remain in this position of intercourse until each has reached a point, at least once, of
having to stop the action to attain Control. The Control Yantra or Mantra combination should be brought
into use by *both* partners whenever either *one* of them
signals for a cessation of movement to attain Control.

By doing this, sexual intercourse can continue almost indefinitely—under the Control of both partners.

After each has attained Control at least once in this
position, the Female should remove the penis from
her vagina and lie beside the Male.

They should now begin to pursue their sexual pleasure
in whatever way they wish. The Tantric Masters recommend that alternating the active and passive roles of
sexual relations makes the maintenance of Control
somewhat easier, and prolongs the pleasure even further.

For example:

The Couple disengages from the Woman Above
position. The Male kisses, stimulates, fondles, masturbates, and performs cunnilingus on the Female, pausing each time she seeks to maintain control. (If she
is accustomed to, or desires, multiple orgasms, she
may alternately maintain Control, then "let go.")

The Male may then turn his body over to the Female, as she in turn may concentrate on kissing, fondling, masturbating, and oral stimulation of the Male,
remembering to respect *his* desires for Control, and
stopping her actions at whatever point he signals her
that he needs to attain Control.

The same signaling and cessation of movement while
Control is sought applies to whatever position of sexual
intercourse you use, be it the Man Above or on your
side, or rear entry, or seated on a chair or literally
whatever your imagination can conceive.

All that is important is that *Control Be Maintained*. And, by practicing Control, in every lovemaking situation, Control becomes easier to attain and maintain.

Add sexual foreplay and intercourse itself can be prolonged as long as you wish.

Then you can indicate when you are ready for orgasm, and it can be brought on when desired, in the manner desired.

More of the nuances of this ultimate Control in Tantra are discussed in the chapter following this on "Continuation" and in the "Special Rituals section."

After you both have been sexually satisfied, you should lie close together, entwined, bringing your Channeling Yantra and Mantra into focus as you relax together.

Then you may return to the table and finish the bottle of wine and food, and talk about your love and lovemaking, communicating openly and honestly.

You have now completed the Seventh Night of the Tantra. But it is a beginning point, not a termination.

And as you sleep tonight, the Channeling Mantra and Yantra will bring forth more of what you seek from life.

A CONTINUATION

And the Tantric Master sent forth the new Tantriks with these words:

"You walk the earth beneath your feet in a new way. The Essence of your being is now known unto you.

Through that Essence, you know great pleasure and power, which you now master.

"Now you are at the beginning; newly born in the ways of the Tantric Life. From your Essence, you shall create and master each new step you take, for the pathway is not trodden down, it is ever new. Your arrival at the summit of enlightenment shall be by your own pathway, unguided by another.

"The Rituals you know shall take on new power and energy as you continue to practice them.

"Each day of Tantric Life shall bring greater knowledge of self and of others; greater capacity to know pleasure and give pleasure; greater energy and mastery of it; greater Control over your life, your being, and all that you discover within this universe. For you shall be one with yourself, one with the earth, one with all others, one with the universe, one with the essence of all being.

"And your essence shall grow and open the way to the touching of all immortal essences, that exist on planes where existence shall be made known to you.

"Take each step with assurance that it shall be pleasant beyond any pleasures other mortals know.

"For you exist as an essence of pleasure; your body, the Key to all creative forces. You are separate, yet now you are a part of the union of all essences that have ever existed or ever shall.

"The power, the pleasure, the mastery of all shall be revealed to you."

The Seven Nights of The Tantra, and the Rituals for Females and Males individually, have provided the basic concepts of the Tantric Sex, leading to greater enhancement of your sexuality, greater awareness of yourself and partner, Control of the vital energies of sex, and the ability to channel those energies into all areas of life.

Each day, the basic Yantra imagery of all the exercises should be brought to mind and focused upon. Time should be set aside for the yantra, as a form of Tantric concentration. For with the yantra, you maintain the Control and the ability to Channel.

The rituals themselves should be a scheduled part of every day.

If at all possible, the basic elements of the Couples' Rituals should be practiced.

On any given night that the couple is apart, or there is no opportunity for practicing the rituals as a couple, the solitary rituals should be carried out, including the Control Ritual.

When you have sexual relations, you should adhere to the basic awareness that your relationship is now a Tantric one and should include repetition of Controls and Channeling within your lovemaking, not only to reinforce the Controls, and to use constantly the Awareness and Channeling, but because each reinforcement of Control brings more Control, and heightens sexual ecstasy even further.

The next section of this book deals with "Special Rituals and Notes on Tantric Sex." When these are studied, it will be made even clearer the myriad ways in which the Male, Female, and Couples' Rituals may be carried even further, for the enrichment of sexual pleasure.

Now you are in Control of yourself, and your sexuality and your future. If at any time you feel that Control is slipping, go back to the basic exercises and intensify your use of them; use the yantra imagery and mantras every day.

During a time of solitary quiet, close your eyes and,

using imagery alone, without touching yourself, say the Awareness Mantra and carry yourself through the Male Alone or Female Alone Rituals. The imagery alone will recreate your sensations of awareness and, after a while, your sensations of excitement and stimulation; and your Control will assert itself; and the Channeling will follow.

This yantra and mantra part of the Tantra can become a very basic part of your life.

Having Control of all aspects of your sexuality, you will find yourself more in Control of all areas of your life.

As you pursue the practice of the rituals, each day will bring new pleasures, and greater awareness of the calm confidence within you—calmness and confidence created by your knowledge of self and powers you have achieved as a Tantrik.

SPECIAL RITUALS AND NOTES ON TANTRIC SEX

PREFACE

The basic Male, Female, and Couples' Rituals are not the whole of Tantric Sex.

Among the many volumes written over the last thousand years, there are repeated references to other rituals and comments on many aspects of sensuality, sexuality, Awareness, Control, and Channeling.

Each ritual is designed to focus on one particular aspect of Tantric development, be it a further development of awareness, or the procedures for attaining prolonged orgasm, or the exercises necessary for perfecting the muscular coordination of the vagina (known as the Tantric vagina).

To any Male or Female in sound physical condition, there is no reason for any of the rituals to be physiologically harmful as long as they are carried out as directed.

Not all students of Tantra may wish to make use of the rituals in this Special Section. This is fine. The basics of Tantra are fully covered in the Male, Female, and Couple's Rituals. Utilizing only those sections, you may master the three fundamentals of Tantra: Awareness, Control, and Channeling. Indeed, it is the *mastery* of the Alone Rituals that is the basis of Tantra.

But the serious student should read this Special Section in its entirety, to become aware of the comments of the Tantra on a wide range of subjects, and to know of the further rituals from which you may choose to enhance your Tantric abilities in a specific area.

The Tantra says that such specialized rituals as those dealing with erection should prove beneficial to the Male, not just to cope with instances of impotency but to aid in attaining erection repeatedly in a given period of time.

Likewise, the Tantric texts see the development of the Tantric Vagina by the Female as an important adjunct to her increased Awareness and her increased ability to give and receive pleasure.

Other rituals are designed to help further break down self-consciousness and inhibitions.

Once you have completed the Female or Male, and Couples', sections of this book, you will have become a *Tantrik* who now proceeds to master the basic concepts, and develops further aspects of Tantric Sex and Power.

NEW PARTNERS

The Tantra does not make moral judgments.

It presumes that those who were promiscuous before becoming Tantriks will probably remain promiscuous; that those who were moderate in the number of different partners with whom they had sexual relationships shall most likely remain moderate; and that those whose life is centered around one partner will continue in that manner.

Because of the very nature of the Tantra, you will likely initially learn it with one partner. Once you have mastered the solitary and couples' exercises, you may remain together, or go your separate ways.

But the Tantra will have had its effect on you as an individual. The Tantric approach to a sexual relationship, however long, however short, makes the Tantrik the natural "teacher" and controller of the relationship.

The Tantra says that if a Tantrik chooses a new partner, the Tantrik should make known to that new partner the Tantric ways. Of course, if the new partner is also a Tantrik, then the relationship will be Tantrically oriented from the beginning.

If the new partner is not a Tantrik, then it is up to you to preserve your Tantric concentration by showing the new partner the Tantric way. If the Tantrik shows his or her new lover the heightened joys of Tantric love, that alone will make the new lover want to study Tantra. The Tantrik can then begin instructing in the Alone and Couples' exercises, making the new partner a Tantrik also.

The Tantra is most emphatic about the beginning of a relationship with a new partner.

It says:

If the Female takes to herself a new lover, she must, in every way, insist on her control of their lovemaking during the initial period. This requires communication, and great Control on the part of the Female. She should not hesitate to demonstrate her developed Awareness, abilities, and Control, to heighten the joys of her partner.

Equally, when the Male takes a new partner, he should insist on demonstrating his Tantric ability to give his partner the greatest possible pleasure and satisfaction.

The ways of maintaining the attitude of "teacher" to "pupil" need not be blatant. They should in fact be quite subtle. But the Tantrik, says the Tantra, must be the leader, and maintain his or her control of the love-making.

To the true Tantrik there is no desire to "convert the world" to Tantric ways. But neither is there any thought of abandoning the ways of the Tantra, once they have been mastered.

THE TANTRA AND AGE

"That the mind is supple, not the body."

That is Tantric text's way of saying, "Age is not important."

It does not matter at what age the student begins studying the Tantra, only that the mind be receptive to the Tantric concepts, open and willing to believe and try. Tantric groups often begin teaching the Alone Rituals to their children at about age twelve. Such instruction is intended to condition the adolescent to a Tantric approach to sex; an open, honest, uninhibited approach. There are no taboos. There is only free communication and instruction regarding knowledge of one's body and sexuality. It is a form of instruction that, according to Tantric texts, leads to greater self-confidence and freedom from many of the "problems of sex" which create adolescent tensions and frustrations.

In one of the texts there is the story of a Tantric man of eighty-six years, who nightly entered into the joys of Tantric lovemaking with his "older wife," who had taught him many years before.

The story continues that the wife died at age eighty-nine, and the Male Tantric took unto himself a younger wife, not a Tantrik, whose age was sixty-three, and he taught her the ways of the Tantra and she was reborn sensually and sexually and in all areas of her living.

And when the older Male Tantric died at ninety-one, his "younger wife" took herself a lover aged forty, and taught him the ways of the Tantra, and their bliss lasted through all the years they were together.

It is likely not a literally true story, but it brings across two points relative to the Tantra:

Age is not a factor in learning.

Age is not a factor in enjoying the pleasures of the Tantra.

My own research into Tantra included interviews with a fairly large number of Tantriks. The youngest among them was nineteen. The oldest was seventy-eight. And they ran the gamut of ages in between.

Each said, in so many words, that age was not important, but that maintaining an open mind, and practicing the Tantric rituals, were absolutely essential.

Man and woman, says the Tantra, too often allow their lives to become embroiled in the small-but-urgent (and emotionally and physically draining) matters of each day. They soon begin to place more emphasis on the world about them than the world within them.

And in doing this, they push deep inside all the beauty within themselves that is there for the knowing; and they allow their inner power to slip away.

The flow of sexual energy, says the Tantra, is the flow of life, and life-creating energy. Stymied, it ceases to flow and is locked inside.

But, if allowed to flow freely, its forces will multiply and the creative energies will become the power to create.

To Control the flow of sexual energy is not to block

it; rather, the Control allows us to direct and channel the energy; to live our lives to their fullest, enjoying each day by enjoying the powers within us; using the powers within to give and receive pleasure with another and with the world.

Not only is age not a factor in Tantric living and loving, but the Tantra itself is one of the keys to a long life.

FEMALE MULTIPLE ORGASM

The Tantric texts point out that the Male strives, in sexual relations, toward the point of a single orgasm and ejaculation. The Female may likewise strive toward only one point of orgasmic satisfaction, or she may experience more than one orgasm.

The Tantric texts go further and divide the Female into three classifications called *Vegas,* determined by the achievement of orgasm:

1. *Chanda-Vega:* The Female who achieves multiple orgasm easily, or as a matter of course, within her sexual relations.

2. *Madhyama-Vega:* The Female who, either by preference or proclivity, strives for only one orgasm during a given sexual encounter.

3. *Manda-Vega:* The Female who rarely achieves even a single orgasm.

For the sake of clarity in interpreting the Tantra in modern terms, we shall refer to these as Types One, Two, and Three, and discuss each in turn, along with Tantric comment and suggestions.

Type One: The use of the Tantric Awareness exercises should serve to increase the pleasure of the repeated orgasms. By *Controlling* orgasm at its onset during sexual relations, then relaxing the control, the *intensity* of the orgasms will be increased. The Tantra recommends that this type of woman should practice the Special Ritual dealing with the vaginal orgasms, as well as development of the Prolonged Orgasm, and the Tantric Vagina.

Type Two: The Tantra states that this type may, by preference, not wish to experience multiple orgasm. If not, then she should at least utilize the Control of her orgasm several times during each session of lovemaking—approaching orgasm, then backing away (Prolonged Orgasm)—and thus intensify her single orgasm into one of greater ecstasy, power, and energy.

The Tantra suggests that this type practice the Prolonged Orgasm Ritual to achieve this goal.

But, says the Tantra, this type should not dismiss the possibility of attempting multiple orgasm. In solitary Control Ritual she should bring herself repeatedly to the threshold of orgasm, then attain control. Once this is easily done, she should practice the Awareness Rituals and imagery, either alone, or with a partner, to increase her stimulation. Then, with a partner, in a Ritual similar to the Seventh Night of the Couples' Rituals, she should communicate with her partner the desire to achieve multiple orgasm. The Male masturbates her to the point of orgasm, then stops while she gains control; then the Male masturbates her until she achieves orgasm. Both partners should maintain Control as they continue fondling and foreplay. Then the Male should stimulate all areas of her body orally, culminating in cunnilingus to the point of orgasm, then stopping until control is attained. Then the Male should repeat the oral stimulation of her body. He should continue cunnilingus until a second orgasm is achieved; after which, slowly, the Male should begin Awareness stimulation of her body again, manual and oral, leading to sexual relations and her third orgasm.

Once this multiple-orgasm exercise is agreed upon, the Male must maintain absolute control until the Female has achieved her third orgasm in succession. The Female, once committed to trying this exercise, should allow herself to be stimulated repeatedly, even though in the past she has only had one orgasm.

Once the exercise is completed and the Female has experienced three orgasms in one session of lovemaking, she may likely wish to try for four. At any rate, she should try the exercise and achieve the triple orgasms on at least three occasions in one week before deciding whether or not she wants to make repeated orgasms a part of her Tantric lovemaking.

She may, even after successfully achieving multiple orgasms, decide that she prefers a single orgasm.

Type Three: Even two thousand years ago the Tantra refused to acknowledge the existence of what some people call a "frigid" person. They believed, as do modern psychologists, that there are only inhibitions which need to be removed.

The first two Female Alone Awareness Rituals are designed to bring about a better understanding of your own body and its sexuality and sensuality. These exercises are of the greatest importance to this type of woman.

Further, she should concentrate on the yantra imagery of awareness with great dedication.

And, as she does her daily solitary exercises, the Tantra strongly suggests that she add one further step:

Alone, once each day (regardless of her other sexual activity), she should go through all the Awareness exercises and proceed to masturbate herself to orgasm.

In the conditioning process of Tantra, orgasm begets orgasm. The more orgasms one experiences, the more easily they are achieved.

If in solitary practice she is unable to achieve orgasm through masturbation, she must overcome her self-consciousness and explain this, as a simple fact, to her partner.

Despite the inability to achieve orgasm, this woman should enter into the Couples' Rituals with her partner.

Each night after finishing the prescribed ritual, and after the one hour has passed, they should proceed to the bedroom and once again the Female should allow the Male to watch as she performs the Awareness Ritual and the Control Ritual, in which she masturbates herself. But this time, she should not fight for controls. She should allow her masturbation to carry her to orgasm.

With the Male watching, her inhibitions will be removed, and that may help her reach orgasm.

If it does not, the Tantra says the Male should attempt "whatever he can envision" to help her reach orgasm. Some of the Tantric texts tell of the use of the dildo; others, the use of a soft feather to tickle and tease the clitoris and perineum and anus. In more modern context, there is nothing wrong with the Male or the Female herself using a vibrator to help her achieve the initial orgasm.

Once one orgasm is achieved (and if enough variations are tried, it *will* be achieved), then it is just a matter of substituting her own masturbation to orgasm in place of the original system, using the Awareness

Mantra and envisioning the yantra of whatever imagery she fantasized for the first orgasm.

From her own successful masturbation, the steps of Tantra are logical for reaching successful orgasm through being masturbated by her partner, then through cunnilingus.

At that point, she may proceed through the exercises described to achieve multiple orgasms.

Each Woman in the world is different. Time and the use of Tantric Awareness, Control, and Channeling are the keys to successful achievement of multiple orgasms, as well as all the delights of the Tantra.

ERECTION

Erection is usually attained by the Male during the course of sexual foreplay and anticipation.

But occasions do occur when erection is difficult.

The Tantra attributes these occasions to fatigue, stress, and nervousness. Modern psychologists tend to agree with what the Tantriks learned long ago: that a relaxed attitude toward difficulty in maintaining erection is one of the keys to resolving the problem.

First, the Tantra says, if the Male has just engaged in sexual relations and achieved orgasm, he should not *rush* to attain another erection. The approach should be slow and leisurely, allowing time for the regeneration of energy.

If the Male is unable to achieve erection at the beginning of sexual activity, the same slow, leisurely attitude should be assumed. The Male's partner will no doubt be as aware of the problem as the Male is, and her attitude should likewise be a leisurely one.

Whatever the cause of the problem, the goal is to achieve erection, and Tantric texts recommend the following:

The Male should lie on the bed nude in the Awareness Position. He should relax and concentrate *not* on achieving erection but on the imagery of Awareness. He should say three Awareness mantras.

His partner should sit on the side of the bed, quietly, without touching him. She should be on his *left* side facing his feet, her buttocks alongside his waist.

The Male should slowly slide his hands down his abdomen to the base of his penis. His right forefinger and thumb should encircle the penis at the base. His left hand should cup his testicles.

Now he should concentrate his imagery, eyes closed, on the muscular contraction exercise. He should envision his penis with all its muscles and the "empty tubes" inside the penis itself.

He now squeezes together the finger and thumb encircling the base of the penis and slowly begins to pull upward, away from the base, his fingers maintaining pressure—a pulling-sliding action toward the end of the penis. At the *same time* he should contract the muscles tightly and envision their contraction in his imagery, which also includes his "seeing" the tubes filling.

His action—the contraction, the sliding of the encircling fingers, the imagery—should all be coordinated simultaneously: the time he holds the muscular contraction should be the length of time it takes for the encircling fingers to slide the length of the penile shaft.

When the encircling fingers reach the glans, the muscular contraction should be relaxed and the penis should be released. The Male should then relax for a moment.

Now the same action should be repeated again: encircling, pressure, pulling-sliding of fingers from base to tip, coordinated with the muscular contraction.

Now the act is repeated a third time, then the Male returns his hands to the folded position on his abdomen.

He maintains his position, eyes closed.

Now the Female looks down at the Male's genitals. Her *right* hand now moves to the base of the penis; forefinger and thumb encircling the base. Her left hand cups and gently massages the testicles—slowly, only the testicles.

Her forefinger and thumb squeeze around the base of the penis.

When the Male feels her squeezing pressure, he initiates a strong muscular contraction.

When she feels the Male's muscular contraction, the Female slides-pulls her encircling fingers along the shaft of the penis, to the glans. Because she is squeezing with pressure, there is a sensation of her "pulling" the penis; *but,* as the Male did, she should squeeze with only enough pressure to allow the encircling fingers to slide slowly up the shaft.

When she feels the Male's contraction relax, she releases the penis. She is *never* to *slide* the fingers back down the penis to the base. She should let it "fall" to its natural position.

Again the Female encircles the base of the penis; the Male does his contraction when ready, the Female slide-pulling the penis along the shaft toward the glans, the Female relaxing her grip on the penis the moment she feels the contraction relax.

The action is then repeated the third time.

Now the Male straightens out his legs on the bed and opens his eyes. He and the Female relax while three Awareness Mantras are silently repeated.

Now the Male turns over on his stomach. The Female does not move, but as the result of the Male turning over, she is now on his *right* side.

The Male now raises his hips and slides his knees under him, raising his shoulders and resting his weight on his elbows and knees, in an "on all fours" position. Once he has assumed this position, he should spread his knees as far apart as is comfortable, fold his arms and allow his head to rest on his arms.

The Female should be able to reach her left hand around the Male's right hip and, from the rear, "cup" his testicles in her left hand.

Her right hand now goes, palm up, under the Male's stomach; the palm sliding along his abdomen toward the penis; her hand now turning so that once again she may grasp the base of the penis in the encircling grip of her forefinger and thumb.

The Male now concentrates on the muscular contraction Yantra imagery and contracts the muscles.

As soon as the Female is aware of the muscular contraction, she should begin the pulling-sliding movement from the base of the penis toward the glans. Because of the Male's position, the movement of her hand will be a "milking down" motion.

In Tantric texts, this is literally called "milking the penis to erection."

Her downward, pulling-sliding action should cease the moment she feels the Male relax his contractions. Again, she must *not* slide her fingers back along the penis from tip to base.

Physiologically, erection is attained by the usually

empty "tubes" within the penis filling with blood, which
causes the penis to grow in size and harden to an erection.

This "milking down," coupled with the muscular contractions, creates a "drawing force," along with "grav-
ity," to help the filling process necessary for erection.

The Male should go through three muscular contractions, the Female milking down the penis each time,
then releasing it.

After the third contraction, the Male should cease his
contraction exercise and remain in the "all fours" position, concentrating on the sensations created in his
body by the Female's actions.

After the third contraction is relaxed, the Female
should continue the milking action. Even when the
penis begins to grow and harden, she should continue
the milking action from the base to the tip of the penis,
never sliding the fingers back along the shaft from tip
to base.

At the same time, the Female should use her left
hand to continue massaging the testicles, moving her
hand occasionally from testicles to perineum to rectal
muscles, slowly and gently (never fast or frantically)
adding stimulation.

When the Male begins to respond to the milking-
down exercise, he may raise his head and "stand on his
knees" on the bed.

When he does this, the Female releases both her
hands from his genitals. She then changes from a seated
position, to a position lying on her back on the bed;
her feet toward the head of the bed; her head below
the Male's genitals.

The Male now leans forward again, to rest on his
elbows. The Female's vagina is now just below his face,
adding stimulation for him. He is also now in a position

to touch the female's genitals, embrace her hips, open the vaginal labia, and kiss the clitoris—whenever he wishes.

When the Male leans forward, the Female will find her head is directly beneath his genitals.

Raising her left hand, she can stimulate his testicles, perineum, and anal muscles.

With her right hand, she immediately uses the index finger and thumb to reach up and encircle the base of the penis again. She continues the "milking down" procedure.

When she reaches the end of a downward "milking" and releases the penis, she raises her head as she moves her hand back to the base of the penis. When her fingers encircle the penis base, she allows the penis to slide into her mouth as far as possible. She closes her lips around the penis, then she creates a *strong suction* on the penis. She holds the suction and at the same time begins to milk downward the penis with her fingers allowing her hand to push her mouth off the penis while holding the suction.

This procedure should be repeated over and over.

If you "kiss" your forearm with suction, you will find the skin has turned crimson due to the drawing of blood toward the area by the kissing suction. The same will happen in the penis. The milking downward creating a flow of blood toward the penis, the oral suction drawing the flow into the "empty tubes," and causing erection.

The sensation for the Male is far from clinical. The milking-down action is extremely stimulating, especially when coupled with the fondling of testicles, perineum, and anal area.

The sucking-downward on the penis is an exquisite sensation.

And there can be little doubt that erection will occur.

The Male can use his muscular contractions, whenever he wishes, to add to the process of erection. He will also have the Female's genitals before him. And, if he so desires, he can bend his head "down" and look "up the female torso" to watch the erotic milking-sucking process.

The whole exercise is so stimulating to the Male that many prefer it as a part of their lovemaking, particularly the "second time around."

Of course, once the erection is achieved, the Male and Female may wish to continue in this position of mutual fellatio-cunnilingus; or the Male may turn over on his back, the Female atop him, now in a position to continue fellating the Male, and to move her vagina into the position she prefers as the Male orally stimulates her.

They may, as they wish, make this a totality of lovemaking, or alter their positions to have sexual relations in any manner they wish.

It should be noted that, in using this exercise for attaining erection or lovemaking, many Males enjoy adding aspects of the Anal Stimulation Ritual. This, of course, is purely a personal choice, to be mutually decided upon by the partners.

There is little doubt that this Ritual will serve the purpose for which it was evolved: the attaining of erection.

THE TANTRIC VAGINA

One of the primary teachings of the Tantra is the development of what is known as the "Tantric Vagina," which is an extension of the Female Alone Ritual of muscular contraction and control.

In that Ritual, emphasis was placed not only on the contractions themselves (the physical aspect of the exercise) but on the associated Imagery of the vagina as a tunnel or passageway surrounded by layers of muscles, which indeed it is. It was assumed that the exercise would be practiced alone, and that it would also be practiced under the circumstances set forth in the Couples' Ritual where the Contemplative Position was introduced and the exercise was practiced around the Male's finger inserted into the vagina.

This was further extended in the Couples' Ritual when the muscular exercise was practiced after the penis · is inserted into the vagina with the Female in the Woman Above position.

The Tantra states that the exercise should be continued on a regular basis in all three manners. Practicing will enable the Female to contract the muscles more easily, and to precisely determine just which muscles she is contracting without having to contract all of the related abdominal and thigh muscles. She will also reach a stage of being able to retain the contraction for extended periods of time.

It is this combination of abilities that make the Tan-

tric Vagina, which can greatly heighten the sexual
pleasure of both the Female and the Male.

By tightening the vaginal muscles, the Female can
bring the inner walls of the vagina into more complete
contact with the entire shaft of the penis, adding greatly to the frictional sensation of intercourse.

The tightened muscles grasping the penis can send
the Male into spasms of ecstasy.

With this muscular control, the Female can maintain the movement and coordination necessary for the
Tantric Vaginal Orgasm.

This ability is considered one of the greatest achieve-
ments of Tantric teaching. Yet it is relatively simple to
achieve, requiring only cooperation between the partners, and persistence in the exercises leading to it.

First of all, the Female should practice *daily* the
muscular contraction. It should be a part of her Tantric Ritual. But further, she should practice the contractions themselves many times during the day. One
suggestion is that the contractions be done *twelve* times
between rising in the morning and sleeping at night.
This is not excessive, given the fact that three contractions can be held and released in a matter of one to
two minutes.

Secondly, the Female should discuss the Tantric
Vagina and its development with her partner. They
should make the exercise a part of their mutual Tantric
ritual.

The practice of this Ritual, involving the Male, will
give him so much pleasure that he will hardly refuse
to work with the Female to develop the Tantric Vagina.

In the course of foreplay or the Rituals of the
Tantra performed by the couple each night, there is a
natural point at which the Male inserts his right index
finger deep into the vagina, to stimulate the Female.

There should be three long contractions of the vagina on the finger.

At yet another point in the Ritual or foreplay, the Female should assume the Woman Above position and the Male should lie very still while the Female goes through three contractions around the penis.

At the third contraction, the Female should contract the muscles as hard as she can and at the *same time* rise slowly. At first this will be a matter of her rising off the penis and it coming out of the vagina. However, as the muscles' strength develops, it will be a sensation as if, grasping the penis with the vaginal muscles, she is lifting the male up by pulling on his penis.

At the point in Ritual or foreplay where the Male Above enters the Female, he should lie very still for a minute once his penis is deep within the vagina and allow the Female to practice the three contractions again. As she contracts for the third time, the Male should slowly withdraw his penis from the vagina while she is maintaining the contraction.

Here again, at first this will simply be an exercise of the Male's withdrawing while the Female contracts the vaginal muscles. But after the muscles have reached a certain point of development, it will be as if the vaginal muscles were grasping the penis, holding it in place, and refusing to permit its withdrawal—trapping it.

This can become one of the most pleasurable parts of your sexuality.

After a while the Female will be able to control the muscles for sustained periods of time, and with much stronger power.

In the Tantric texts are stories of the development and results of the Tantric vagina. It is written that the development can reach such a state that the vaginal muscles can be constricted so tightly that, at the point of orgasm the tightness around the penis can prevent ejaculation. And even after the male has had an orgasm and his penis has decreased in size, the vaginal muscles can hold it in a vise-like grip so it cannot be withdrawn from the vagina until the Female permits it by relaxing the muscles.

The muscles of the vagina, like any other muscles of the body, can be strengthened by exercise. It is not unreasonable to accept at face value the stories the Tantra tells of the development of the totally powerful Tantric Vagina.

All that is required is persistence.

VAGINAL ORGASM

The Tantra acknowledges that the center of Female sexual pleasure lies in the clitoris, and that the Female reaches orgasm through stimulation of the clitoris, and other erogenous areas.

However, Tantric texts devote considerable comment and suggestions to the concept of the vaginal orgasm—the reaching of orgasm without clitoral stimulation at the time of orgasm.

Tantric texts relate the success of vaginal orgasm to the development of the vaginal muscles and the following procedures:

When in the course of lovemaking, the Female decides to have an orgasm (and it is a "decision" because Control is maintained), and she wishes to begin developing the ability to have vaginal orgasms, she should allow herself to be stimulated in whatever way she wishes and, by prior arrangement and discussion with her partner, she should have her partner lie on his back on the bed. She should then assume the Woman Above position—straddling the Male's pelvis. *She should face toward his feet* and lower herself onto the penis, inserting it well into the vagina. Then she should begin whatever pelvic movements bring her the most pleasure and stimulation.

In this position, the clitoris will not contact any part of the Male's body (as it does in this position when she faces the Male's head).

If she cannot, through pelvic movement alone, approach orgasm, she should move her fingers to her clitoris and stimulate it. *But,* the moment she feels orgasm approaching, she should remove her fingers from her clitoris, intensifying instead her pelvic movements, and free of any clitoral stimulation, begin the vaginal muscular contractions which will create additional friction between the walls of the vagina and the penis. These contractions should be repeated as fast and often as possible, held as long as possible, and coupled with the most stimulating pelvic movements.

The impending orgasm should then build slowly and take place without any clitoral stimulation at all.

If this exercise is somewhat fatiguing the first few times it is tried and the feeling of impending orgasm begins to fade, the Female may renew, *briefly,* the stimulation of the clitoris, ceasing such stimulation when she again feels orgasm approaching; returning to total emphasis on moving her hips in the manner most stimulating, and combining this with the muscular contractions.

Many Tantric women have developed the ability to reach this vaginal orgasm. Their claim is that attaining it is not difficult, and that it affords a depth of sexual pleasure quite different from the normal clitoral orgasm,

This becomes easier with practice.

There is another approach to attaining vaginal orgasm, which can be alternated with the method described above.

In this second method, when the Female wishes to experience vaginal orgasm, and is in a sexually stimulated state, she lies on her stomach and raises her hips slightly. The Male places his penis in her vagina from the rear. He moves his penis in the vagina, directed by the Female's pelvic movements. He does *not* lay the full weight of his body on the Female's back, but rather rests his weight on his arms and knees, allowing the Female to move freely.

The first few times this is attempted, the Female may use her hands to stimulate the clitoris until she feels the approach of orgasm, then cease all clitoral stimulation and begin the muscular contractions around the penis as it moves within her and as she moves her hips to increase stimulation.

If the Female prefers the Male may reach around her waist, slide his hand down her abdomen, and use the forefinger and thumb of his right hand to stimulate her clitoris initially—but the Male must keep in mind that the Female is not seeking clitoral orgasm. As soon as she feels orgasm approaching, she should grasp the Male's arm to signal him, and he should immediately withdraw his hand and *cease* all clitoral stimulation.

The Male should likewise use the Control Mantra and imagery to control his own sexual excitement while the Female goes through the musclar contractions and reaches orgasm.

The Female will, once stimulation ceases, begin the contractions and movement as she did when she was in the Woman Above position, until she reaches orgasm.

By practicing this regularly, the conditioning for bringing about the vaginal orgasm will be achieved, and developed to the point that entry of the penis in the vagina, when the Female is coupled with the Male in either of the positions suggested, will bring the process of building toward vaginal orgasm, without any further clitoral stimulation than that which was a part of the foreplay that created the initial sexual excitement. Once the position is taken, and the contractions begin, the orgasm will occur without any clitoral stimulation.

PROLONGED ORGASM

For the Female's pure sexual enjoyment, this Ritual is considered by the Tantra to be as important as multiple orgasm and the "joys of the Tantric Vagina." For the Male, the prolonged orgasm will bring about a great heightening of sexual pleasure, allowing him to engage in sex for as long as he wishes.

The prolonged orgasm is self-defining. It literally seeks to have the usually short-duration orgasm extend over a period of time. The texts cite instances of Female orgasm lasting for ten minutes or more—a single, continuing orgasm spanning that length of time without ceasing. Male Tantriks have been known to reach a point that, from the beginning of orgasm and ejaculation, to the completion of ejaculation and orgasmic sensation, "may last a duration of ten to twenty minutes."

The key to attaining the prolonged orgasm lies with the Control Ritual.

The Tantra states that the Female and Male should have practiced that Ritual faithfully, as well as have mastered all aspects of *Control* in the Couples' Ritual, before attempting to master the prolonged orgasm.

The test of whether or not you have "mastered" the Control Ritual and the Control of the Couples' Rituals is a simple one: Can you stop yourself, while masturbating, on the very verge of orgasm and return to a Controlled condition without having the orgasm? Can you, with your partner, stop yourself and gain Control just prior to orgasm, whether your partner is masturbating you, performing oral stimulation, or having intercourse?

If you have been able to allow yourself to approach orgasm, then cease the stimulating activity, and *using the Control Mantra* and *imagery* attain control without actually having the orgasm, then you are ready for this new Tantric experience, the prolonged orgasm.

It is emphasized that you *must* be able to utilize the Control Mantra and Imagery as your means of Control—that you Control by *saying* the Mantra and by *writing* the Mantra on the black void of your imagery. In doing this, all concentrative effort goes into Control and you can stop yourself at whatever point you wish.

With this firmly in mind, go through the Control Ritual alone, following all the instructions. As you feel the impending orgasm, switch to Control Mantra and imagery, and cease masturbating. The female should leave her hand lying relaxed atop her vagina; the Male returns his hands to their relaxed position on his abdomen. Using your Controls, attain absolute Control, so that you know and feel the impending orgasm will *not* occur; then, as soon as the Control is attained *securely,* relax your Control and begin to masturbate again. You will find yourself in such a stimulated state that very quickly you will feel the approach of orgasm again—at which moment you cease to masturbate, and turn on your Control Mantra and Imagery, to attain Control gain. Once Control is again securely maintained, begin again to masturbate. Repeat this process until you have experienced the impending orgasm *nine times.* Once you have maintained the control nine times, then on the tenth time, give yourself over to the orgasm. It will be an intensity unlike any you have ever before experienced from masturbating.

You may (if you have a most cooperative partner) allow him or her to masturbate you in this exercise, but, if you do so, he or she *must* be understanding of your objectives and willing to cooperate by ceasing the stimulation the moment you signal to stop, so you can gain Control.

For the first few nights, solitary masturbation is preferable. Alternately, you may each go into a separate room and practice the Control Ritual, bringing yourself to the verge of orgasm nine times, and attaining Control nine times. Then your partner may join you and bring you to orgasm in whatever way you wish.

You should do this every night. Each succeeding night, and each succeeding time within the Ritual that you masturbate, you should try to bring yourself closer and closer to actual orgasm, and at the same time make sure, no matter how close you approach orgasm, that you pull back into Control.

After a while, you will be able to use the Control Mantra and imagery like a "switch" to turn on and off. As you masturbate, closer and closer to orgasm, you will find that, by merely stopping the masturbating and switching, quickly, to the Control Mantra and the written Yantra imagery in your mind, you can stop the orgasm and exercise complete Control.

Once you exercise this Control, you can return to masturbating more quickly—then return to the Control, more quickly—switching the feeling of impending orgasm on and off with your mind.

After a while, you will find that, when you switch on your Control Mantra and imagery, you will not actually have to stop masturbating, if you slow down the stimulation, but continue to masturbate while at the same time calling on the Control Mantra and imagery. See just how *close* you can come to the verge of orgasm. Stop masturbating only when you feel you are literally about to have the orgasm itself. Then concentrate completely on Control.

Once you feel that you have strengthened your ability to control orgasm by stopping it just as it is beginning, you may move to the final phase of the exercise.

Repeat the exercise as on previous nights. Three times come to the verge of orgasm, then attain Control, and then repeat the process.

On the fourth time, slow down your stimulating activities, making them slower and slower as you near the verge of orgasm. When you feel the orgasm is about to begin, allow the first spasms of the orgasm to begin; *then,* when the orgasm and the first release of ejaculation has started, cease all stimulation and use the Mantra and imagery of Control. This will require great willpower, and an instant switch-on of Control. But it will work—and you will be able to stop the orgasm even after it has begun.

You will find that then you can turn off Control, stimulate again, and the orgasm will resume. When it does, turn on Control and cease stimulation. Repeat this process for as long as possible, then give yourself over to the orgasm.

Once you have mastered this technique, you will find that you can actually turn the orgasm off, then on, by using the Mantra and imagery, *even* though you continue the masturbatory stimulation.

You can cause the orgasm to cease, then start, at will, so long as you continue to masturbate. And the orgasm will not lessen in intensity and "end" until you relax Controls. For the Male, this will not only prolong the sensation of orgasm, but also control the length of time for complete ejaculation of the semen.

Once this is mastered, you can do the same on-and-off Control procedure to prolong, for as long as you wish, the orgasm when your partner masturbates you.

You can then proceed to Control the prolonging of your orgasm while being orally stimulated, as well as when having intercourse.

Many Tantric women who perfect this prolonged orgasm prefer it to multiple orgasms.

Faithfully followed, the instructions of this Ritual can prolong the orgasm "for as long as the Tantrik wishes to tolerate the intense joy it sends through her body."

Unlike the prolonged female orgasm, where there is no objective way of "proving" that it works (only the description of it by the female Tantriks who have mastered it), the prolonged male orgasm can be objectively studied.

And, under observation by witnessing Tantriks, it has been seen that the time from the first spasm of orgasm and first ejaculation by a masturbating male Tantrik, to the final spasm of orgasm and final release of ejaculate, lasted a duration of twelve minutes; and the penis remained erect and obviously in orgasm for the full twelve minutes' duration.

The male Tantrik, according to his own statements, required "several months of intense practice" to attain mastery of the prolonged orgasm.

Many male Tantriks seek to achieve this prolonged orgasm of Tantra and consider its attainment one of the great goals of Tantric Sex.

ORAL SEX: FELLATIO

In Tantric Sex, oral stimulation is a natural sexual expression. The techniques of fellatio are generally understood by the Tantrik.

Oral sex should be openly discussed so that the partners fully understand the pleasure given, and in which ways it may create the most stimulation.

The rhythm of the movement of the mouth on the penis should be sustained and repeated for several minutes, then changed, to prolong the act itself. It is recommended that the movement of the head, to facilitate the penis sliding in and out of the mouth, should be alternated with "holding" just the glans in the mouth, and encircling it, around and around with the tongue; then with the tongue flicking "with definite force" the opening at the end of the penis.

At the time of movement of the head from base to tip of the penis, there should be applied an ever-increasing amount of suction, in addition to the movement.

Then the Male should devise a signal to alert his partner that Control is required to prevent orgasm at a given time. When such a signal is given, the mouth should slide away from the base of the penis, keeping only the glans inside. Then the lips should be stretched tightly over the front teeth and the glans pressed tightly between the lips, to "squeeze" the glans, creating the numbing sensation that aids the male to control and prevent orgasm. Then the process of fellatio can resume. In this way, oral stimulation of the penis can go on indefinitely, without orgasm occurring involuntarily.

From time to time during fellatio, the penis should be removed from the mouth and it should be "nibbled at" with the teeth exerting pressure but not "biting pain" around the glans and along the underside of the penis, on either side of the "outline" of the urethra.

Likewise, a "nibbling" and suction can be applied to the testicles.

"Deep Intake"

The idea of allowing the penis to penetrate far down the throat during fellatio is not a new one.

To accomplish this, you should breathe simultaneously through both the nose and mouth to prevent any gagging sensation.

Lift your head "back" into a position that aligns the throat and mouth, thus allowing the penis to slide into the back of the mouth and down the throat without "bending."

Realistically, some mouths and throats are quite simply too small to accommodate some penises.

In such cases, the concentration of fellatio on the glans, and the nibbling and tonguing aspects, should be emphasized, and the deep intake not attempted.

But, with cooperative effort, the deep-intake method of fellatio can be accomplished by many Tantriks.

The Ejaculate

Most medical spokesmen agree that the ejaculate (semen) from a healthy Male is not injurious when take into the mouth or swallowed.

This is, of course, a matter of personal choice.

Quite often inhibitions about fellatio are initially overcome by the partner's knowledge that the male Tantrik is always in control and, if his partner wishes, the Male can agree not to ejaculate, and can Control the orgasm.

Once the initial inhibitions that may exist concerning fellatio are overcome, the additional inhibitions concerning semen and other aspects of fellatio may also be overcome.

ORAL SEX: CUNNILINGUS

Tantric texts discuss oral stimulation of the vaginal areas, as follows:

The lips should be used with a "nibbling" movement around the exterior of the vagina; along the inside of the thighs, where they join the genital area; around the pubic hair, the mons veneris, and the labia.

The same areas may also be stimulated with a tracing or licking with the tongue.

One at a time, the left and right outer labia should be "sucked" gently into the Male's mouth and stimulated simultaneously by the tongue. The same should also be done with the inner labia.

The tongue may then probe the vaginal opening, as far as possible.

Special emphasis is placed on locating, and stimulating, the urethral opening, about an inch or so below the clitoris. This should be done with a flicking motion of the tongue over, past, and "into" the opening.

Of course, the clitoris should get the most attention.

The stimulation, by the tongue and lips, of all areas around the clitoris should create an indirect stimulation of the clitoris itself. If initially the stimulation purposely *avoids* the clitoris, then the sensations of the clitoris when it *is* stimulated will be more intense.

The clitoris should be licked, with backward and forward motions. Then the clitoris should be sucked gently into the mouth between lips closed around it, and the tongue should create a "flicking" movement across it; then again use the licking movement; then sucking and flicking; thus alternating and heightening the stimulation.

If the Male is facing downward, he should put his left arm around the Female's hips and use his left hand to fondle her buttocks, hips and thighs. His right hand should be placed on her vagina, just below his head; the right thumb inserted into the vagina and the right index finger used to lightly stroke the perineum and rectal opening.

If the Male is facing upward, while lying with his body between the Female's legs, he may extend his left hand upward, sliding it along her abdomen, to fondle her breasts. His right hand should move to the vagina, the right index finger inserted in the vagina (hand palm down), and the right thumb used to stroke the perineum and rectal opening.

The subtle variations are innumerable and depend on individual desires. As in all aspects of sex, the Tantric texts recommend experimentation, and open, honest communication between the partners to determine precisely the most satisfying methods.

ANAL STIMULATION

Tantriks are reminded, prior to engaging in anal stimulation, of what the Tantric texts have to say about the care of the fingernails, to avoid pain, and about genital cleanliness, which includes the anal area.

Anal stimulation brings about relaxed, pleasurable sensation at the entrance to the rectum. The Male or Female lies on the stomach in a relaxed position, eyes closed, and concentrates on the *feelings* created by the stimulation itself. The partner being stimulated should focus concentrated imagery on an image of the rectal muscles and, with deliberate thought control, imagine the muscles themselves relaxing. The yantra image should be of the actual muscles, relaxing. The Tantrik who tries this will find that the muscles do indeed begin to relax, though their usual reaction to stimulation is a tightening.

The partner should part the cheeks (cleavage) of the buttocks and lightly stroke the area, in long, even strokes.

He or she should kiss the entire area of the hips, with the tongue lightly passing over the anal area, in brush-like strokes. These strokes should increase in strength as the mouth slides over the rectal muscle area. Then concerted pressure should be placed upon the muscles themselves. Initially, the passive partner will respond with a contraction of the muscles, but with proper exercise of imagery plus slow stimulation by the active partner the muscles will begin to relax.

At the point where the muscles are beginning to relax, the active partner should massage the muscles with the right index finger, which has been lubricated with a petroleum jelly. (In olden times, butter from goat's milk was recommended because it did not tend to dry out readily. The same is true of petroleum jelly, as opposed to a water-soluble lubricant which may dry out very quickly.)

The introduction of pressure against the muscles at the entry to the rectum should be very slight. It should be a circular motion, gradually moving toward the center of the rectal muscles themselves. Very slowly the index finger may be inserted into the rectum. Each movement inward should be very slow and deliberate.

The passive partner, with relaxing imagery, should allow the muscles to relax to permit the finger to enter the rectum. If it is difficult to relax the muscles, then the passive partner should "strain outward" with the rectal muscles, like straining outward of a bowel movement. This will relax the muscles and permit the finger to enter easily.

Little by little the finger should move deeper into the rectum. It is only in the first inch or so that resistance will be felt. Because of the pleasure this brings any initial resistance will be relaxed and the finger may enter its full length.

Once within the rectum, the finger should remain relatively still for a few moments.

Many women have never experienced anal sex because of inhibition and fear of pain. The inhibitions should be overcome with the exterior stimulation and anilingus. The fear of pain may well be offset by the pleasure of conditioning.

Once the index finger is well within the Female's rectum, she should slowly turn over on her back while her partner keeps his finger in the rectum.

Once on her back, the partner's finger should be turned palm up, so that the natural position of the right thumb will be on the vagina. In such a position, the partner should use the right thumb to stimulate the clitoris and vagina as the index finger moves slightly within the rectum.

In such a manner, the Female should be masturbated to orgasm.

If practiced often enough, this exercise will bring about a conditioning of pleasure associated with anal penetration, and eventually the Female will be able to experience anal orgasm without the clitoral stimulation, because of the intensity of sensation within the rectum.

Even two thousand years ago, the Tantric writers were aware that there was "within the length of a finger inside the Male an organ which can produce a special pleasure and is an aid to erection." That is the old Tantric concept of the prostate gland.

And the Tantra was right on both counts.

In order to adequately stimulate this remarkably sensitive gland, the passive partner should, once the finger is well within the rectum, lie calmly on his stomach. The active partner should insert the finger as deeply as possible into the rectum, the hand turned palm downward. The interior of the rectum at this depth is smooth and rather "hard." The prostate gland is not immediately discernible except that, when reached, it has a "different feel" from the rest of the rectal wall. No particular pressure need be applied to the area. Merely touching it is sufficient.

It is this stimulation within the rectum that, in many Males, is considered a definite aid to erection at times when erection may be difficult.

And at those times when erection has already been achieved, it adds considerable stimulation and a definite heightening of pleasure.

Anal Intercourse: As in all matters concerning the anus as an erogenous area, the idea of anal intercourse is immediately rejected by many persons.

Many medical authorities warn that anal penetration may be injurious if the muscles are torn in the process, particularly if hemorrhoids are present. It is therefore emphasized at this point that anal intercourse is not being recommended, either by the author or by Tantric texts. This section merely offers Tantric suggestions should the couple have already determined that they are going to engage in anal intercourse, or have previously made it a part of their sexual practice.

If anal intercourse is attempted, lubrication of the penis and the rectum is important, to allow easier penetration. It is the opening of the anal muscles (about one or so inches) to permit the passage of the penis into the rectum, that creates discomfort.

This should be accomplished gently and slowly.

Many Tantriks engage in anal intercourse and develop the ability, by coupling clitoral stimulation with the act, to cause a form of anal orgasm.

Whether the couple desires to try it is purely a personal matter.

MENSTRUATION

The "old wives' tales" and taboos about sex during menstruation were dismissed in the Tantric texts as "the foolishness of the unwise."

The "blood red center" of many of the Tantric Icons is a symbol of menstruation, related to a heightening of psychic sexual energy levels when intercourse is performed during menstruation.

In many women, the period of menstruation is often accompanied by a raised libido, and sex should be enjoyed without interruption during it, say the Tantric texts.

No natural bodily function is considered taboo by the Tantric texts.

And specifically, the Tantric texts state that all of the Awareness Rituals and the Control Ritual should be practiced during menstruation, as at other times— without interruption.

Likewise the Couples' Rituals should not deviate during menstruation.

And the raised libido, if it does occur, should find satisfaction during the period as at all other times.

In short, there should be no "bending" to the old taboos for the Tantrik.

TANTRIC PSI

Psi is a modern term generally used to label paranormal or extrasensory experience.

Tantric texts are filled with stories of use of the Tantric Power of Channeling to increase the Tantrik's ability in this area.

They tell of the Tantric Masters who control others through thought transference (mental telepathy), which creates certain dream sequences within the subject's mind.

The entire field of Hindu *Vashikarana,* "the control of another's will and thoughts," has developed from Tantric studies using the basic Channeling ritual and progressing into paranormal areas with it.

Many of the authentic fakirs of India use the same yantra imagery to control the usually involuntary organs of their body, to control pain, and to develop concentration to levels most people believe to be unattainable.

Through a mental channeling of their energies, Tantric Masters have been able, according to the texts, to bring each other to orgasm even when they are physically separated.

The texts also tell of the Masters who "through the power of Yantra and Mantra" created energy levels of such magnitude that they could "project their essence across mountains and seas to any place they desired to be." This is, of course, the phenomenon known as Astral Projection of Out-of-Body Experience.

It would require another book to explore all facets of the use of Tantric Energy in attempting paranormal experience.

This is a subject with which I am now experimenting and conducting extensive research. I am convinced that the link between Tantric Power and Psi Paranormal Experience does exist.

TANTRIC YOGA

Tantric Yoga is best defined as a more sexually oriented form of Hatha Yoga.

Tantric Yoga is a physical discipline which incorporates varied sexual positions. Its philosophies are based, to a large degree, on Tantric teachings.

It is not only difficult to define Tantric Yoga, but also to determine just how "Tantric" it is.

Many "gurus" who teach so-called Tantric Yoga are in reality ascetics who are more accurately teaching the rigid disciplines of Hatha Yoga, with sexual position exercises added to the routine. They still insist on the meditative aspect of Hatha Yoga, and on the separation of body and mind.

Such teachers are not, in a true sense, teaching anything "Tantric."

On the other hand, I have found a few groups (usually informally organized) who study "Tantric Yoga" and *do* incorporate their interpretation of the Tantric Rituals and Doctrines in their studies. They do *not* teach ascetic disciplines. Rather, they are far removed from the Hatha Yoga doctrines. They have taken basic Yoga and removed any ascetic philosophy, turning instead to the search for unity of body and mind, as taught with the freedom granted in pure Tantra.

In the Tantric Texts there exist certain physical exercises which are the *real* Tantric Yoga, if Yoga is accepted as "a physically oriented discipline" and no more.

The Contemplative Position" outlined in the Rituals, and the position used in the Alone Rituals, might well be described as Yoga positions.

For example, in the Tantric texts, there is the following "Yoga-like" exercise:

The purpose of this exercise is to provide a new sensation to heightened sexual stimulation and orgasm. All Tantriks would benefit, say the texts, from spending at least one half hour per week standing on their heads—to reverse the bodily flows, including the pumping attitude of the heart.

In this specific sexual exercise, the Female, with the Male's assistance, stands on her head, preferably against a wall, her shoulders and buttocks touching the wall, her legs straight up. She maintains this position for several minutes, with the Male helping her if she is not adept at headstands.

The Male massages her breasts while she is in this position; then he parts her legs and stimulates the perineum, labia, and clitoris. Once the Female becomes aroused, the Male may (as determined mutually before the exercise began) either continue to masturbate the Female to orgasm, or begin to stimulate her orally and bring her to orgasm by cunnilingus. The entire objective is that orgasm is attained in this position, to add yet another aspect to the Tantric experience.

The Male likewise should try standing on his head and being manually or orally brought to orgasm.

It will "add a dimension to sensation of which the Tantrik has never before dreamed."

This exercise could correctly be considered "Tantric Yoga."

The difference actually lies not in what the position is, but rather in the underlying doctrine that accompanies it.

In this volume, I have attempted to include interpretations only of the Rituals that apply to true Tantric Sex, and the reaching of Tantric goals—not the gray areas which may lead to confusion.

CONTRACEPTION

Because the primary Tantric teachings are designed to heighten sexual response and enjoyment, the use of contraceptive methods is endorsed. Sexual pleasure and energy have a Tantric purpose and are procreative only when desired.

The teachings include several specialized exercises, centered around the Control Ritual, for use as contraceptive methods. These include the highly touted system of actually directing the male semen into the bladder on ejaculation, rather than permitting it to pass normally through the urethra. But some medical opinion holds that this, over a prolonged period of time, may have dangerous side-effects. For that reason, it is not included in this book.

Additionally, Tantric Yoga has a series of Yoga sexual positions developed to "lower the probability of conception." But they are far from foolproof and rightfully belong in a book on Tantric Yoga rather than here.

Interpreted in the light of modern medical and psychological knowledge, Tantric teachings would endorse the use of any form of contraception, be it the Pill or mechanical means, such as a diaphragm or sheath.

If mechanical contraception is used, it should be made a part of the ritual of lovemaking.

The placing of the sheath on the penis by the Male's partner can be a very erotic part of the ritual of sex. So, too, can the placing of the diaphragm into the vagina, or the insertion of contraceptive creams or gels.

The couple's feelings about contraception should be a part of the communication about sex which the Tantra so strongly advocates.

THE SETTING FOR SEX

Though the bed may be *the* most ideal place for sexual relations, it should not be the *only* place.

Male and Female receive their primary stimulation from each other and from the source of all stimulation, the mind. Certain sights, sounds, textures, and smells can add greatly to the stimulus by creating an idyllic setting for sex.

Just as the natural odors of the human body heighten sexual desires, so too can the smell of the sea, or the sound of the waves on a beach; the movement felt on a train or plane; the "forbidden" aspect of a certain setting, such as a drive-in movie, or out in the woods.

The Tantra recognizes that the ambience may provide a heightening of sexuality, and therefore endorses the idea of sexual foreplay, or conducting the entire sexual ritual through to orgasm, in as many places as the couple can imagine and arrange.

Within one's own dwelling, the Tantra reminds us, can be found many varied settings: on pillows on the floor of the living room; on a favorite couch or chair (especially for trying new positions); on the patio (preferably if it is an enclosed private one); by—or in—a swimming pool; in the shower or bath.

It is entirely up to the couple *where* as well as *when* sexual relations are carried out.

It is recommended that, as often as possible, the couple deliberately arrange in advance that their sexual encounter will take place somewhere *other* than the usual setting.

CHAKRAPUJA: THE TANTRIC "ORGY"

This is an ancient, highly organized Tantric Rite, attended by a number of Tantriks who, according to the texts, engage in the enjoyment of the five things forbidden in high-caste Indian society: meat, alcohol, fish, certain grains, and total sexual abandon.

The sexual aspect of the Chakrapuja is still practiced in some informal Tantric groups.

Sexual encounters are encouraged between all who attend the rites, and the encounters are usually "controlled" by the acknowledged Tantric Master, who directs the activities of a few of the group. The "few" may be one couple, or several. They perform rituals as instructed, or display for the onlookers their mastery of some special Tantric Feat.

In turn, others "perform."

By controlling the activities, there is a generation of sexual energy among the spectators, and a regeneration of stimulation among those who have reached orgasm and, in turn, watch.

Any Tantrik present may request the privilege of performing any act with one or more of those present. And the Tantric Master consents if those selected agree.

It is an "orgy," in a sense, yet it is controlled and ritualistic, which most catch-as-catch-can orgies are not.

Tantric teachings discuss at length the Chakrapuja, but attendance is not mandatory. Many Tantriks prefer the solitary rituals, or sexual activity confined to one partner, or one partner at a time.

But this "group sex" idea is quite common as an added dimension of sexual expression and generation of sexual energy.

In one Chakrapuja I attended, most of the activity was in groups of three, though there were at times as many as six persons involved in a group sexual act.

Probably the most significant part of the evening was the ritualistic air that pervaded all activity. There was a sense of Tantric Control in everything done.

In the threesomes there was a "two on one" attitude, with two persons giving sexual pleasure to one, then rotating the process. And the same "controlled attitude" persisted, even when six were involved.

That such encounters remove inhibitions is obvious.

Whether the Tantrik chooses to attend remains a matter of personal preference.

STUDYING THE TANTRA

This book is intended as a modern interpretation of the goals and methods of Tantric Sex, divested of mysticism, legend, history, and the esoteric doctrines of Tantra.

There may, however, be readers who would prefer now to study the Tantra "intact."

There are many good books which discuss the teachings of the Tantra, or you may wish to search out translations of the Tantric texts, themselves. A variety of Hindu (yoga) and Buddhist philosophies also include Tantric ideas.

Basically, Tantric teaching relies on a vision of cosmic sexuality—the continual process of union and creation that is the universe and all that lies beyond. It is not a religion. It is an "approach to understanding self, and through self, the world and the universe." It sees Man and Woman as unhappy because of lack of self-understanding, and it seeks to guide them through rituals of *action,* back to their own origins.

Through a maze of symbolic thought patterns, Tantra leads each person back to the identity of his own essence, as it was at the dawn of Creation itself.

Tantra teaches that Man and Woman, basically one, must cast off anxieties and the shackles of society-dictated convention and seek their own independent attitudes by which they can live. To do this, the Tantrik pulls together all the energy of his mind, emotions, and body, through their most common meeting point, sexuality. And with sexuality as the transporter, Man and Woman can move forward to true enlightenment.

By repeating processes, we learn; by repeating procedures, and deliberately forming a ritual around them, we can drastically alter ourselves, our lives, and our enjoyment of both.

The study of Tantra will take the reader through its own Genesis of the world's Creation; a totally different concept of Time and the space Man occupies; and its own highly symbolic view of the world, and of Man and Woman.

The continuous re-creation of time, the world, and Man and Woman, is at the center of the symbolism. The trip upward to enlightenment is mapped carefully, and can be reached. Many have arrived. But it must be sought and experienced. It will not come to those who passively wait, no matter how hard they study the map.

The Tantra carries the student forward into further study of yantric-imagery and the symbolic icons of which the Shri-yantra is the most complex, and most powerful.

At the center of the Shri-yantra is the "dot of female power," the point from which the universe was created. The icon contains upward pointing (male) triangles, and downward pointing (female) triangles, whose interpenetration spreads into lesser angular designs symbolizing the definitive areas of the "reality" we know in this world.

These defined areas of our "reality" are merely extensions of our minds, which are in turn only parts of the essence that is the whole.

It would be presumptuous to try to put into a few words, or even a few pages, all of the knowledge and ideas included in the thousands of volumes that have been written on Tantra.

We could speak here of the self-creating Yoni (vulva) and the anointing of semen by the Lingam (penis); the role of Kali the Creative Force as Kali the Destroyer, who must be destructive in order to create; Shiva, as male energy, and Shakti as female energy; the subtle body; the ebb and flow of psychic energy through the body's chakras—and hundreds of other concepts, all a part of Tantra.

It is obvious, from mentioning these few, that the study of Tantra is a separate pursuit which cannot be contained in one small area.

But as you experience Tantric Sex, you will inevitably desire to know more of the doctrines of Tantra.

And the more you experience all of the Tantric Doctrines, the more your life will be changed, for you will understand your being and its essence.

Formal Studies

As such, there does not appear to be an "ashram" solely for Tantric study. However, there are some groups whose studies have incorporated much Tantric teaching:

Vajrayana is the "extreme" form of Tibetan Tantric Buddhism. Small groups of believers may be found in many larger, more general, Buddhist study groups. They usually have informal meetings and must be sought out. They never seek publicity or try to convert anyone. They believe that those who are seriously in search of their teachings will find them (which is not always the case).

Many of the Hindu groups also incorporate Tantric teaching. But one must check into the specific group carefully, for there are some Hindu (yoga) groups whose teachings are ascetic and therefore strongly *opposed* to the Tantra. To them, as to many religious groups, Tantriks are outcasts.

Once you have studied the Rituals in this book, I suggest that you read one or more books on the doctrines of Tantra. Then, if you wish to find a group, do the following:

Locate a "Buddhist Center" or a "Tantric Yoga" center or a "center" for religion or philosophical studies (which exist in most major cities of the world), and represent yourself as "a Tantrik who wishes to learn more of the true meanings of Tantra in the pursuit of enlightenment."

If there are any Tantrically oriented groups within the centers, you will be directed to them and can easily determine, from what you now know, if they are what you are seeking.

If the centers are ascetically oriented, that will be obvious after a brief discussion.

Should you not have access to such centers of study, then I suggest you obtain as many written works as possible on Tantra and begin your studies. Discuss what you are studying with your partner and your friends.

It takes only two people to form the nucleus of a study group. Others who are interested will join you and you may soon have your own center of Tantric studies, where the interpretation of Tantra and Tantric Sex can be a focal point of common interest, leading to fulfillment of common goals.

If you wish, you may direct any questions you have to me, care of the publisher. I will try to answer as quickly and completely as possible.

CONCLUSION

Awareness. Control. Channeling. Yantra imagery. Mantras. These are the basic ingredients of Tantric Sex, and they comprise the basis for the Tantrik's heightened enjoyment of sensuality and sexuality—and the control of all facets of her or his life.

To the Tantrik who will study this book and practice its rituals, the rewards will soon be self-evident.

The book itself is intended as a guide, for repeated reference and daily use, just as the Tantric pursuits themselves must follow a daily ritual.

There are two other points which should be made, if the reader will indulge the author a few more lines:

It would be of invaluable aid to me, if those of you who follow the rituals herein and become true Tantriks, would write to me, in care of the book's publisher, with any comments you wish to make.

And because there is now being set up a modern Tantric study center (still in the organizational phase as this is written), the author will attempt to reply to any inquiries concerning the location of the center, or centers, as soon as the information is available.

The Tantra says:

"Man or Woman may never deplete the power within, for it is infinite, its abilities unlimited; its joys continually increasing."

May you know the joy and the power of the Tantra.

BIBLIOGRAPHY

Garrett, John. *Tantra*. Five collections of stories. The
    legends of Tantra. Bangalore: Mysore Government
    Press, 1865.
Sadagopachariar, M. C., *The Third Story of Tantra*. A
    study of Tantric meaning. Madras: Chettiar, 1889.
Mudaliyar, Tandavaraya. *Tantra: Panchatantram*. Interpre-
    tation of rituals. With English translation and annota-
    tion. Madras: Chettiar, 1891.
Tantrakhyayika: The Tantra. A collection of Hindu tales
    in its oldest recension, the *Kashmirian*. Legends and
    rituals. Translated by Dr. Johannes Hertel. Harvard
    Oriental Series, vol. 14 (1915).
Shrichakrasmbhara Tantra. The Buddhist Tantra, edited
    and translated by Kazi Dawa-Samdup. Tantric teaching
    as related to Buddhism. London: Luzac & Company,
    1919.
Sastri, Kapali. *Further Lights*. The Veda and the Tantra.
    Interpretation of Tantric Myths and Rituals. (British
    Museum Reading Room 4508aall. 1951).
Woodroffe, John G. *Creation as Explained in the Tantras*.
    (British Museum Reading Room 4504-g.45; 1915).
Tantras: Recherches sur la symbolique et l'energie de la
    parole dans certains textes tantriques. A study of Tan-
    tric texts, symbols and energy. Paris: L'Institut de Civ.
    Indienne, 1963.
Tantrākhyāna. A collection of Indian tales. Edited, trans-
    lated, and annotated by C. Bendall. Stories related to
    Tantric Doctrine and Ritual. *Journal of The Royal
    Asiatic Society*, vol. 20, part 4, p. 466–501. London:
    Sansk. & Eng., 1888.
Mahānirvāna Tantram. A translation edited by Manmatha
    Nath Dutt. Interpretation of Tantric Doctrine and
    Ritual. Calcutta: H. C. Dass, 1900.

Avalon, Arthur. *Tantra: A Translation from the Sanskrit.* The "purest" Tantric translations. London: Luzac & Company, 1913.

Hevajra Tantra. 2 vol. Original texts and translation. Sanskrit and Tibetan texts. A complex translation of the first Tantric texts by D. L. Snellgrove. London: Oxford University Press, 1959.

Panchatantra. Translated from the Sanskrit by Arthur W. Ryder. A basic translation and interpretation. Chicago: University of Chicago Press, 1925.

The Panchatantra. Translated from the Sanskrit by Franklin Edgerton. A slightly different interpretation. London: George Allen and Unwin, 1965.

Hitopadesa Stories and the Panchatantra. Translated by A. S. P. Ayyar. Ritualistic parables, myth, and interpretation. Madras: V. Ramaswamy Sastrucu & Sons, 1960.

Winfred, S. *Tamil: A Tantra Translation.* Madras: 1873.

Rice, Stanley. *Indian Fables and Stories from the Panchatantra.* London: John Murray, 1924.

Tantra: Text and Teaching. Translated by P. J. Sasparasi. The most lucid description of the rituals and their purposes. Calcutta: Sasparasi, 1901.